Doing math in

Morning Meeting

150 Quick Activities

THAT

Connect TO Your Curriculum

Andy Dousis AND Margaret Berry Wilson

Introduction by Roxann Kriete

All net proceeds from the sale of this book support the work of Northeast Foundation for Children, Inc. (NEFC). NEFC, a not-for-profit educational organization, is the developer of the *Responsive Classroom*® approach to teaching, which fosters safe, challenging, and joyful elementary classrooms and schools.

ISBN: 978-1-892989-37-6

Library of Congress Control Number: 2010928741

Book design by Helen Merena
Illustrations for cover and introduction © Lynn Zimmerman, Lucky Dog Design. All rights reserved.

Northeast Foundation for Children, Inc.
85 Avenue A, Suite 204
P.O. Box 718
Turners Falls, MA 01376-0718

800-360-6332
www.responsiveclassroom.org

Third printing 2012

Printed on recycled paper

The authors would like to thank their respective spouses, parents, siblings, children, and their many students and teachers.

They would also like to thank the following individuals: Molly Lippman, Lara Webb, Michael Lain, Alice Yang, Helen Merena, and Paula Denton.

Finally, the authors would especially like to acknowledge Roxann Kriete for her exceptional vision, inspiration, and insight that culminated in the creation of this book.

Contents

Math Belongs in Morning Meeting

by Roxann Kriete
author of The Morning Meeting Book

A couple of years ago I visited a school that had been implementing the *Responsive Classroom®* approach to teaching for several years. I was hugely impressed by my observations there and was enthusing to a friend upon my return. As I described some of the Morning Meetings that I had seen, I spoke of the ways students listened to each other, the thoughtful questions they asked about each other's sharing, and the delight they took in the wordplay that their teachers had embedded in the morning messages. I was off and running about the vocabulary development that I'd seen happening and the language skills that were flourishing at every grade level during these twenty- to thirty-minute whole-class openings to the day when my friend—who happens to love, promote, and teach math at every opportunity—interrupted. "And did you see any math going on?" His question stopped me for a moment as I reflected. I had to acknowledge that I had not seen any math in the meetings I'd observed.

Over the next months I repeated his question to many of my colleagues who work with teachers and are in classrooms far more frequently than I am. They related some terrific stories of classes collecting, charting, and discussing data about aspects of classroom life. A great example was the Life of a Pencil in Room 3B Project, which served the dual purposes of math development and lessons on the conservation of a precious classroom resource. My colleagues also told stories about activities that students clamored to "play" that developed fluency with math facts or encouraged deductive reasoning. But overall they relayed that these were exceptions, and that it was not common to see math skills embedded in Morning Meetings.

Yet we all agreed that Morning Meetings abound with opportunities for math infusion—for fun and lively skills practice or conversations demonstrating ways in which math skills apply to all aspects of our daily lives. During Morning Meetings, children greet each other, share news and observations, do an

1

activity together, and read a message from their teacher that launches them into the rest of the day's learning with curiosity and confidence. Young children can send a "good morning" skipping around the circle, greeting every second or third or fifth classmate. Older students can share current events that involve math or play a game that requires them to build equations.

To help teachers regularly incorporate math into their Morning Meetings, Northeast Foundation for Children decided to create a book that would provide practical ideas for teachers to use. As co-authors Margaret Berry Wilson and Andy Dousis and I embarked upon the project of gathering ideas for this book, we found ourselves walking through the world with a heightened sense of math awareness. Listening to the economic news on the radio on our commutes to work, we wondered, "How many zeros are there in a trillion? And how many ways could that number be represented?" When the morning newspaper announced that the town's police budget must be cut by $150,000, we found ourselves wondering, "Just how significant a number is that? Is $150,000 a big number in this context?" Suddenly, math was everywhere. Consider this story from Margaret:

> *Recently, I was standing at an airport baggage claim area when a large ceiling tile fell and grazed my left shoulder. At about the same time as I felt the tile, I realized that a very large brownish-black rat had also been on top of it. The rat seemed as surprised to have landed there as I was to see him. It began scampering among my startled, screaming fellow passengers.*
>
> *I had a different, perhaps odd reaction: My brain immediately turned to math. How big was the ceiling tile? How much did it weigh? How close was the tile to hitting me directly on the head? How long was the rat? What was its speed as it scurried about? What percentage of people were now standing on chairs? (Later I also wondered, "For every rat one sees in an airport, how many rats are in the ceiling?") I felt trapped in some version of Jon Scieszka and Lane Smith's book Math Curse, but at least my math obsession kept me calm during a strange ordeal.*

We also found ourselves remembering our own elementary school math experiences, musing about what had engaged us and developed our sense of ourselves as competent mathematicians. I remembered a particular turning point for myself. In elementary school, while reading had always seemed to me full of mysteries and questions to ponder, math had appeared to be at best a rather orderly affair, full of numbers to line up and rules to learn. I accepted this as important, but it didn't inspire much wonder. And then came the spring day in my sixth grade year when two classmates and I had raced through our assigned worksheets and were vexing our teacher with the predictable sixth-grade ways we found to amuse ourselves in our "extra" time. These involved liberal doses of giggling and note-passing and required the cooperation of most of the class, since we sat at opposite corners of the room. As a consequence we were sent to the principal to receive extra math work. We trudged in, expecting more worksheets full of computation "challenges." Instead the principal, a rather progressive sort, pulled an orange book off his shelf and dispatched us to the school library, saying only, "Here, help each other and go as far as you can in this." He added, "For the rest of the year, this is your math work."

We were astounded. We were to work without a teacher present? Share a book and talk with each other rather than complete our work in silence and turn our papers over? This was radical stuff in my school in the early 1960s. Our astonishment deepened when the first chapter plunged us into a base 5 universe. Suddenly three plus three didn't equal six. 10 didn't equal ten. Now there was a concept worthy of wonder. Our wonderings led us into juicy conversations and inventions; they engaged us and made us want to know more.

Fortunately, most math curricula today encourage students to work and wonder together, and teaching math as collaborative discovery, as hands-on exploration, is recognized as a crucial way to nurture students to like math and understand math concepts more deeply.

At a time when researchers are seeing a strong correlation between students' math performance in early and later K–12 grades (Leinwand & Ginsberg, 1), best practices in elementary school math instruction are rightfully receiving a lot of attention. Since the initial release of this book, most states have adopted the Common Core State Standards for Mathematics (see page 12). The National Council of Teachers of Mathematics (NCTM) makes the case well for emphasizing math achievement: "In this changing world, those who understand and can do mathematics will have significantly enhanced opportunities and options for shaping their futures. Mathematical competence opens doors to productive futures. A lack of mathematical competence keeps those doors closed" (NCTM, 5).

Of course, elementary teachers are, by their very nature, door openers for their students. They devote enormous skill and energy to giving their students the tools they will need for productive futures. Yet, while some are like the math-loving friend I mentioned earlier, others of us are less sure about our mathematical competence. In fact, one recent study indicated that elementary education majors have the highest levels of math anxiety among college students (Hembree, 33–46).

We know that in math, as in all areas, we are powerful models and our students are astute observers who take their lessons and shape their own attitudes from their observations of us. Therefore, no matter where we each locate ourselves on the continuum of math comfort or competence, it's critical that we find ways for our students to see us using math and enjoying doing so, both within and beyond the boundaries of math group. Starting with the first moments of the day, the more we suffuse our classrooms with opportunities to count and predict, to collect and analyze data, to wonder together about the relationships between numbers, to spot patterns and trends, the better. This book will help all teachers, including those who call themselves "math phobic," to do just that. This book's classroom-tested ideas for incorporating math into Morning Meetings—in small, specific, and practical ways—will help you prop open those doors to math pleasure and math competence for your students.

Of course, there's always the issue of time to consider as well. How are we going to find more time in our already packed days to teach more math? Well, let's assume that math activities take up an average of one-third of Morning Meetings (a fair assumption if at least one Morning Meeting component involves math on most days), and let's do the math:

$\frac{1}{3}$ of daily morning meeting × 180 school days = 30 extra hours of math time

This is the equivalent of an entire week of nonstop math camp each year. A noteworthy equation!

Morning Meetings and Math

Responsive Classroom Morning Meeting is a lively way to start each classroom day in community. Often described by students as "fun!" and their "favorite part of the day," these twenty- to thirty-minute circle gatherings set the tone for the day and build a safe, engaging climate for learning.

Morning Meetings are an essential part of the academic day, not a prelude to it. They often draw from the curricula of the classroom, sometimes previewing the day's learning, sometimes reviewing skills or information introduced in the preceding days. Morning Meetings promote children's academic curiosity while simultaneously developing and allowing them to practice the social-emotional skills they need for working and learning together.

The Four Components of Morning Meeting

Morning Meetings include the four sequential components described briefly in this section—greeting, sharing, group activity, and morning message. This book includes activities to do in each component.

GREETING

Morning Meetings begin with students greeting each other by name. Ways to do this range from the very straightforward (for example, going around the circle with each student greeting a neighbor: "Good morning, Rhonda," "Good morning, Timmy," etc.) to the more fanciful that involve handshaking, singing, or clapping. Although greetings can incorporate math, the primary purposes of greetings are social and tone-setting. The focus should be on each child's greeting and being greeted warmly. Trying to infuse too many academic skills can distract from its essence. For this reason, this book includes relatively few greetings that specifically target math skills.

SHARING

During sharing, students present news or information that helps the class get to know them. Sometimes the class goes around the circle, each student sharing briefly in response to the same prompt from the teacher, such as "What's one thing you like to do on weekends?" Other times one person briefly shares with the whole group, such as "This past weekend my cousin came to spend the night, and . . . ," and then invites questions and comments from the group. Partner sharing on a specified topic can also be effective. This book includes examples of sharing topics with a math focus.

GROUP ACTIVITY

Group activities are brief, lively activities—from chanting to pantomiming to compiling data together—that review specific skills. Successful group activities are interactive and allow all to contribute at their own level. The group activities in this book emphasize math skills, of course, but because they require interaction, they also teach and reinforce social skills.

For more comprehensive information about Morning Meetings and how to start and sustain them in your classroom, see the resources at the end of this book.

MORNING MESSAGE

During the morning message component, the class together reads a message from their teacher that has been written on large chart paper prior to their arrival. The message, which the children will have also read individually as they trickled into the room that morning, highlights one aspect of the learning day ahead. It is intended to generate the students' excitement and promote their sense of competence. Messages are written as a note to the class, embedding skill work. You'll find many activities in this book that make use of the morning message to strengthen children's math competence.

Why Morning Meeting Is a Great Time to Do Math

Morning Meeting provides high-interest opportunities to apply math learning ■
Morning Meeting doesn't have its own content that must be covered. Instead, the life of the class—its members, its academic curriculum, and the events that affect it—comprises the Morning Meeting curriculum. Morning Meeting therefore provides a wealth of "real life" happenings to which children can apply their math learning. How many pets does our class have? How much trash do we discard in a day? A week? A month? In the upper elementary grades, national and world events find their way into Morning Meeting. For all grades, opportunities abound to count, order, and collect and analyze data in ways that help the class learn about themselves and the larger community that they're striving to understand.

Morning Meeting is a safe time for risk-taking ■ Morning Meetings are a predictable and safe time, well-suited for risk-taking and for students to explain and justify their thinking to others. These meetings emphasize making each other welcome and teach the skills of respectful conversation. Students learn how to articulate news succinctly, how to listen, and how to respond thoughtfully. Within Morning Meetings, these habits of respectful discourse carry over from sharing and responding to personal news to sharing and responding to explanations about how one solved a math riddle or estimated the perimeter of the classroom—an enormous benefit for any student whose confidence about math is shaky.

Morning Meeting allows practice in explaining one's math thinking ■ Math educators are increasingly recognizing the importance of students being able to communicate their math thinking. Morning Meeting is filled with opportunities for students to share ideas and observations. When such talk is math related, students are stretched to organize their math thinking and coherently unpack their thinking to others. As they practice using math terminology, they expand their vocabulary and are able to express math ideas with greater precision. Their peers hear a variety of strategies, and their teacher gains insights into their reasoning.

Morning Meeting links math with pleasure and fun ■ Students associate Morning Meetings with fun activities. The format and content are familiar and a playful spirit reigns, and students look forward to these meetings. Not all students look forward to math time with the same pleasant anticipation. In fact, for those who are math-phobic, the approach of math time can signal stomachaches and the onset of an anxiety that can make it hard to take in information or access what they know. It can help that, in Morning Meetings, math activities often are not even prominently labeled as "math." Instead there is just a discussion following up the morning message that features some numbers or a logic puzzle, or an announcement that "Our activity today is . . ." followed by a game using number cards. The interest and enthusiasm of the group is contagious, and consciously or subconsciously, children learn to associate math with pleasure.

Morning Meeting lets students see that *everyone* can do math ■ Different students shine at different kinds of math activities, and the variety of activities in Morning Meeting makes this visible. The student who has the best idea for how to depict data about how far from school class members live may not be the student who comes up with the longest, trickiest number sentence for "27." Some children are fluent operationalists; some are meticulous observers or unconventional problem-solvers. The teacher's respectful reception of the many different ideas that always emerge from a Morning Meeting circle displays the belief that *everyone* is a mathematician.

How Morning Meeting Math Differs from Math Groups

Math in both Morning Meeting and math groups builds community and teaches academic skills. But a key difference is that Morning Meeting's *primary* purpose is community-building and tone-setting, whereas the *primary* intent of math time is to develop students' math competencies. Bearing that and the following distinctions in mind can help you take full advantage of each time of the day.

1 Math instruction time usually involves a small number of students grouped by ability. Morning Meetings involve the whole class, which will have a much broader range of math abilities. This wide ability range provides both challenge and opportunity. The challenge is to choose math activities that are accessible enough to allow all students a way to participate. The opportunity is that students are able to hear and learn math approaches from a wider range of classmates than they see in their math group.

2 During math time, we observe and guide individual students. During Morning Meeting, we focus upon the group as a whole. While we often notice individual children's understandings or mis-understandings during Morning Meetings, we make mental notes, following up later and usually without mentioning Morning Meeting. We want to encourage students to take risks and to experience a sense of pleasure. Feeling watched and assessed inhibits such unreserved participation.

3 Morning Meeting math is for the practice, application, and extension of familiar skills and concepts. Math groups, while they often include review, are where new concepts and skills are introduced.

4 During math time students usually have access to tables or desks, whereas Morning Meetings take place in an open area. Since students come to Morning Meetings without pencils and paper or calculators, it's a perfect time for mental math, for estimation, and for practice assessing the "ballpark" reasonableness of answers.

What's Special About the Activities in This Book?

The activities in this book were chosen to match the community-, curiosity-, and confidence-building purposes of Morning Meeting, and to be practical to use. Specifically, they all fit the following criteria:

Brevity ■ The activities are easy to explain and quick to do. You'll be doing math in one, maybe two, components of Morning Meeting each day. That means a ten- to fifteen-minute window—sometimes even less—in which to introduce, conduct, and wrap up an activity. Short activities also benefit students who are convinced that math isn't "their thing." Even these students are often engaged and hang in happily for the ten minutes that a group activity or a message chart discussion takes.

Requiring few materials ■ Many activities require no materials at all. Where materials are required, they're simple objects whose care and use are familiar to students—a squishy ball for an interval greeting, pennies to illustrate grouping, or index cards with number statements on them.

Relatively easy to manage ■ Activities were selected for their relative simplicity of management. They do not rely on complicated movements or elaborate groupings and regroupings that require extensive practice and can be a particular challenge to students who struggle with self-control. All activities should be successful as long as you've taught and practiced basic Morning Meeting expectations and done the few specific preparation steps where noted.

Variety ■ Novel ideas and structures, familiar favorites like "I'm thinking of a number . . . ," stand-alone games, and activities that extend from the science or social studies curriculum such as graphing the class's bean plants' growth all have a place in this collection. All can be fun while sharpening students' powers of computing and reasoning.

Emphasis on the familiar ■ Morning Meetings aim to start students' day by reminding them that they are successful learners. So it's important to choose activities that get students to practice or apply skills or concepts they've already been presented with, rather than introducing new content. Encountering new content or grappling with the trickiest puzzle ever isn't likely to inspire confidence for the majority of students. There's a fine balance to maintain, of course, and so we choose activities challenging enough to engage students and convey our high opinion of their abilities, yet not so challenging as to be discouraging.

Emphasis on many right answers ■ Questions that have more than one right answer are excellent for Morning Meeting. How Do We Relate? (see page 157) is a great example. So is the tried and true "How many number sentences can we make for today's date, the 21st?" This allows students to participate at many different levels of sophistication and to learn from each other's answers. In the few cases where there are wrong answers, the activities are designed to move quickly and to make it probable that all students will get correct answers in many of the rounds. We don't choose activities that eliminate anyone from participating.

Getting the Most Out of This Book

There are many ways to use this book. You can go to your grade section and browse for activities that jump out as being particularly well-suited for your class. You can use the grids starting on page 205 to look for activities that involve the specific math skills your class is working on, or check each activity for the NCTM content or process standards that your curriculum focuses on. Alternatively, you can simply page through and look for something that involves the specific math skills your class is focused on right now. Regardless of which way you choose, keep in mind these strategies for getting the most out of this book:

Take time to prepare for Morning Meetings ■ Preparation is as important to successful Morning Meetings as any other part of the day. This means creating a supportive physical environment, including a large enough space for the whole class to gather in a circle (teach students how to move furniture to clear a space if necessary). It also means teaching students the behaviors necessary for Morning Meetings to run smoothly and feel safe for all. How should students move to and from the circle? How should they sit? When do they need to be silent? What's a respectful way to offer a different idea? What if you start to answer and forget what you were going to say? Be sure to model and practice all these behaviors, and then be vigilant that students are following through. (See the resources listed at the end of this book for more on preparing for Morning Meetings.)

Introduce math activities carefully ■ Be sure to gather any required materials ahead of time and consider what skills students may need to review before beginning an activity. Sometimes doing a "pretend" or "practice" round before starting "officially" can be useful. Or you might consider teaching a complex activity over a couple of days. To help you plan, each activity lists previous skills students will need to be successful in that specific activity. In addition, be sure to model and practice these basic prerequisite skills for many math activities:

- What to do when waiting for your turn
- Treating "odd people out" with empathy
- How to roll dice and spin spinners carefully
- Shuffling and drawing cards
- Using measuring tools and math manipulatives

Choose a few activities and do variations on them ■ As co-author Andy Dousis reflected recently, "I used to think I had to know and use a million different activities, but I learned that my class does better with a few good activities than with a new one every day." Once students were familiar with the basics of an activity, he increased the complexity by integrating harder and harder content over time. For example, in the Match Card Greeting activity on page 164, Andy started by having his students match fairly simple expressions to their answers, and as the students gained more and more math experience, the expressions became more and more complex. Of course, the same activity done too many times in a row can become humdrum; your teacher sense will tell you when it's time to shift gears from a numbers game to a data conversation or to a round of Body Math (see page 111).

Look beyond your grade level ■ If you're a second grade teacher, look also in the first and third grade sections for ideas. If you're a fourth grade teacher, browse the third and fifth grade sections. In many cases you may even want to look beyond adjacent grade levels. With some adaptation, most of the activities in this book can be used in multiple grades. Skim broadly to open up many more activity possibilities for your class.

Use, Adapt, Invent, Enjoy!

Whether you use the activities in this book as is, tweak them for an optimal fit with your students' current skills and needs, or use them as a springboard to create entirely new activities, keep in mind the discussions above about what distinguishes Morning Meeting math from math group as well as the characteristics of this collection of activities. No matter which activities you use or how you use them, we hope that both you and your students will experience a heightened sense of all the ways that math surrounds and supports us. May math be a fun and frequent part of your Morning Meetings!

About the Common Core State Standards Correlation

The correlation tables that begin on page 221 enable you to quickly identify the greetings, sharing ideas, group activities, and morning messages that will help you address the math content and practices of the Common Core.

Of course, this book is not intended to serve as a math curriculum and it does not address every Common Core standard or practice. Rather, it provides 150 activities that will help you supplement, reinforce, and expand on whatever curriculum you're using to teach the Common Core State Standards for math.

For ease of use, we organized this correlation for each of grades K–5 in three ways:

By Activity ■ Find the activity you want to do in the left-hand column and then look to the right for the Common Core math standards or math practice areas that the activity can help address.

By Practice ■ The Common Core state standards for math identify eight areas of mathematical practices, such as reasoning abstractly and quantitatively. In this format, find the practice you want to cover on the left and then look to the right to see which activities would help support your teaching of that specific practice.

By Standard ■ For a specific standard, such as 5.NBT.7 (Grade 5: Add, subtract, multiply, and divide decimals), find the standard on the left and then look to the right to see which activities would help support your teaching of that standard.

We hope you find this reference tool useful and that you continue to infuse Morning Meetings with joyful, enriching, and inspiring math activities.

References

Hembree, R. (1990). The Nature, Effects, and Relief of Mathematics Anxiety. *Journal for Research in Mathematics Education,* 21: 33–46.

Leinwand, S., & Ginsburg, A. (2009). *Measuring Up: How the Highest Performing State (Massachusetts) Compares to the Highest Performing Country (Hong Kong) in Grade Three Mathematics.* Washington, DC: American Institutes for Research.

National Council of Teachers of Mathematics. (2000). *Principles and Standards for School Mathematics.* Reston, Virginia: National Council of Teachers of Mathematics, Inc.

National Governors Association Center for Best Practices, Council of Chief State School Officers (2010). *Common Core State Standards for Mathematics.* National Governors Association Center for Best Practices, Council of Chief State School Officers. Washington, D.C.

All Grown Up

NCTM Content Standard:

Number & Operations,
Data Analysis & Probability

NCTM Process Standard:

Connections, Communication

**Specific math content
or skill addressed:**

Data analysis, number
relationships

Component:

Morning message, sharing

Materials needed:

Message chart (for the
morning message)

**Preparing students
for success:**

No special preparation
is necessary.

Vocabulary:

Least, greatest, more
than, less than

How to do it:

■ Include some version of the following as the related task on the message:

How old do you think you will be when you are a grown-up? Write your number below.

■ At sharing time, let students know that today everyone is going to share what age they picked and what they plan to do when they are that age. Model using this sentence frame: *"I think I will be a grown-up when I'm 80. I will plant a big garden."*

■ Have one or two more students practice, making sure that they follow the structure you set out. Then, let everyone share.

■ At the end of sharing, ask students questions to reinforce listening and connections. *"Did you hear any people who had the same ages?"* *"Did you hear any people who will do something outside when they are older?"* *"Did you hear any people who will buy something special when they are older?"*

■ During the message time, ask students why they picked the ages they did. Call on a few students.

■ Then, direct students to help you put the numbers in order. You might begin with the lowest number and continue up by asking questions like *"Do you see a number that is more than that number?"* or *"I see a number that is less than this number but more than that one—see if you can find it."*

VARIATION:

Ask students what age they think they will be when they are "old."

EXTENSION DURING A LATER MATH LESSON:

Guide students to make a graph of the results of the message question. Ask open-ended questions to guide them in discussing the graph.

Grade Level

K

Attribute Train

NCTM Content Standard:

Algebra

NCTM Process Standard:

Reasoning & Proof,
Communication

**Specific math content
or skill addressed:**

Attribution

Component:

Activity

Materials needed:

Attribute blocks, pattern
blocks, building blocks,
buttons, or homemade
shapes

**Preparing students
for success:**

Students should have
familiarity with different
shapes.

Vocabulary:

Same, different,
shape names

How to do it:

- For this activity you can use pre-made shapes, or you can make your own playing pieces. You will need enough pieces for each student, plus yourself, to have one. For the pieces, make several shapes. For instance, for a class of twenty-five students, you might make five circles, five squares, five rectangles, five triangles, and six trapezoids. Among each shape, vary the color, size, and thickness. For example, among the five circles, two can be blue, and three can be red; one can be large, and four can be small; three can be thick, and two can be thin.

- Give each student and yourself a shape.

- Place your shape on the floor close to you. Let students know that the next shape should have one, but only one, thing that is different from yours. Otherwise, it needs to be the same. Ask students *"Does anyone think they have a shape that is different from mine in only one way?"* As students offer suggestions, guide them to check whether theirs will work by looking at what is the same between their shape and yours and what is different. For instance, if you have a large, blue, thick rectangle, a student might want to add her large, blue, thin rectangle. You might say *"Are they the same shape? Color? Thickness? Size?"* For this first turn, try out several possibilities to demonstrate the way the activity will work.

- Once you select a second shape, place it on the floor touching the first shape. Subsequent shapes should be placed next to each preceding shape, so that a "train" is created.

- Continue playing, but subsequent turns should be quicker. As you call on students to share suggested next shapes, take the first shape that will work.

- Play until each student has been able to place his or her shape and/or the students get "stuck." If the group gets stuck—that is, comes to a point in the chain when none of the shapes will work—ask students to think about how you can solve this problem. (Most of the time, shapes can be added at some earlier point in the train or you can start a new train.)

VARIATIONS:

- Once students become adept at this game, try changing two attributes on each turn.

- For more active classes, play music. When the music stops, let students find partners whose shapes have one, but only one, difference from their own.

EXTENSION DURING A LATER MATH LESSON:

Use this as a warm-up game for math time.

Grade Level

K

Beats in a Name

NCTM Content Standard:

Number & Operations,
Algebra

NCTM Process Standard:

Problem Solving, Connections

**Specific math content
or skill addressed:**

Counting, part/whole
relationships

Component:

Activity

Materials needed:

Chart paper (optional)

**Preparing students
for success:**

Students should have
some prior familiarity with
the concept of syllables.

Vocabulary:

Same, different,
chart, counting

How to do it:

■ Let students know that today you will be playing a game with names. Use a made-up first name as an example and clap the syllables in it. Repeat several times with other names that no one in the class has to make sure students understand the concept.

■ Clap the number of syllables in one or several students' first names. Let students guess whose name it could be. For each name, have all students clap with you to see if it fits with the number you clapped. Accept all possible names. You may want to keep track of the number of syllables in students' names on a chart.

1	2	3	4	5
Scott	Andy	Allison	Elizabeth	

■ Repeat until you have included all students' names.

■ Ask students *"If we wanted to clap 7 or 8 times, how do you think we could do it using our names?"* Students might suggest including first and last names; including first, middle, and last names; or repeating their first names several times.

■ Take one of those ideas, like using first and last names, choose one student, and clap that student's first and last names. See if students can identify whose name it is.

■ Repeat for a few more students as time allows, and tell the students whose names weren't clapped to think about how their own names would sound.

VARIATIONS:

■ Play this game with other content area words or words from the morning message.

■ Clap the beats and let students try to find words that fit that number.

EXTENSION DURING A LATER MATH LESSON:

Ask students to figure out the syllables in their full names. (Later in the year, students can use number sentences. For instance, if a student's name is Theodor Seuss Geisel, he would write 3 + 1 + 2 = 6.)

15

Collections Sharing

NCTM Content Standard:

Algebra, Data Analysis & Probability

NCTM Process Standard:

Reasoning & Proof, Connections, Communication

Specific math content or skill addressed:

Sorting/grouping, counting

Component:

Sharing

Materials needed:

Students' collections

Preparing students for success:

About two weeks before you plan on doing the sharing, explain the project to students and send home a note to parents and caregivers (see the example to the right).

Check in with students throughout the week on how they are doing with their collections and be ready to assist students at recess or around the classroom if they have not been able to collect anything at home.

Vocabulary:

Total, sort, categories, types

How to do it:

■ Students share their collections either in an around-the-circle format or through a dialogue share. The dialogue share (in which a few students share each day) works best because students can elaborate more on the mathematical aspects of their collections. Whether it is around the circle or dialogue, set a parameter for some math aspect to the sharing—for instance *"Your sharing needs to tell us how many objects are in your collection and one way you could sort it."*

■ Model, using your own collection. *"I collected seeds from various packets that I had around my house and that I found in the yard and other places. There are thirty-three seeds in my collection, and I have found three ways to sort them so far: by size, by color, and by type of seed!"* Ask students to notice how you shared. If necessary, ask them how long your sharing was to emphasize the importance of brevity. Add *"I am ready for questions and comments"* and let students practice questions and comments on you.

■ Students share and take questions or comments.

VARIATION:

If your school has access to a place that has interesting objects students can collect (rocks, leaves, sticks, weeds), conduct a whole class walk where everyone finds one thing for a class collection. During sharing, everyone shares their contributions.

Dear Parents and Caregivers,

In math, we are working on sorting and counting collections of objects. One way to make these tasks more meaningful for students is for them to have their own collections. So, over the next week, each child should collect many small objects in one category that she or he can then bring to school. For instance, a student might collect rocks, leaves, bottle caps or tops from around the house, twist ties, buttons, used envelopes from the mail, or dried beans. The only rules are (1) the collection should be fairly small so that your child can carry it to school in his or her backpack, and (2) please don't buy anything—have your child collect things from home or in your neighborhood. Thanks for your help!

EXTENSIONS DURING A LATER MATH LESSON:

■ At math time, challenge students to see how many ways they can sort their collections and let them share some of the ways they chose at the end of the lesson. Depending upon how big students' collections are, you might also ask them to draw or otherwise represent one way they sorted.

■ Let students create a display with their collections on poster paper.

Dance with Me

NCTM Content Standard:

Geometry, Number & Operations

NCTM Process Standard:

Communication, Connections

Specific math content or skill addressed:

Counting, measurement, navigational directions

Component:

Activity

Materials needed:

Music (optional)

Preparing students for success:

Students will need some room to move in this activity, so be sure to model and practice how to move without bumping into others. You may also want to clear the space around the circle, if necessary.

Vocabulary:

Left, right, backwards, forward, facing

How to do it:

■ Have all students stand and turn so that they will be able to see and move in the same direction you move.

■ Practice the direction-following aspects of the activity before adding music. Call out some directions, including number, distance, or navigational turns, in a rhythmic way. Here is an example:

Take two steps to the left (clap, clap)
Now two steps to the right (clap, clap)
Take two steps back (clap, clap)
Now three steps forward (clap, clap)

Take three steps to the left (clap, clap)
Now three steps to the right (clap, clap)
Take three steps back (clap, clap)
Now one step forward (clap, clap)

Turn to the left (clap, clap)
Turn to the right (clap, clap)
Touch your toes (clap, clap)
Now face me (clap, clap)

■ If you are going to do this activity with music (something fast and lively works best), add the music and continue.

VARIATION:

Do this activity more formally with CDs or music downloads that feature specific dance instructions (like the "Cha Cha Slide").

Faster, Lower, Higher

NCTM Content Standard:

Measurement

NCTM Process Standard:

Problem Solving,
Communication

**Specific math content
or skill addressed:**

Comparison

Component:

Activity

Materials needed:

None

**Preparing students
for success:**

This activity is very lively
and exciting, so be sure
students have practiced
what to do when you give
a signal for attention.

Vocabulary:

More, less, words
with -er ending

How to do it:

■ Teach students the chant:

> *Put your hands together and tap,*
> *Let's see how _____ you can clap.*
> *Now let's see if we can make it more.*
> *Can you clap _____er than before?*

■ For the first round, choose a word for the blank. Possibilities include fast, slow, low, high, quiet, loud.

■ Practice the chant with movement. As you say the first line, students gently clap their hands together. When you get to the next line, students try to clap according to the attribute chosen. On the last line, students try to go faster, slower, lower, higher, quieter, or louder than previously.

■ Repeat several times with several different attributes.

VARIATION:

Vary the rhyme to accommodate different descriptive words. Here are a few examples:

> *Turn yourself around and about,*
> *Let's see how _____ you can shout.*
> *Now let's see if we can make it more.*
> *Can you shout _____er than before?*

> *Take a step, pointing with your toe,*
> *Let's see how _____ you can go.*
> *Now let's see if we can make it more.*
> *Can you step _____er than before?*

> *Keep your head up—don't let it drop,*
> *Let's see how _____ you can hop.*
> *Now let's see if we can make it more.*
> *Can you hop _____er than before?*

EXTENSION DURING A LATER MATH LESSON:

This is a good activity to do on a day when you are going to explore comparison concepts like "more than," "less than," "longer than," or "shorter than."

Fiddle Faddle

NCTM Content Standard:

Number & Operations,
Algebra

NCTM Process Standard:

Reasoning & Proof,
Connections

**Specific math content
or skill addressed:**

Identifying numbers,
number relationships

Component:

Activity

Materials needed:

Set of standard playing cards

Chart

**Preparing students
for success:**

It will help if students are
familiar with playing cards,
especially the face cards,
so that they will know
the correct card order.

Vocabulary:

One more, one less

How to do it:

- Pass the cards around so that each child has two. Keep whatever cards are left over for yourself and put those face up in front of you. (If you have more than twenty-six students, each child should receive only one card.)

- Ask if any students have 8s. Have one student with an 8 place the card in the middle of the circle. Ask students what number comes before 8 and what number comes after 8. Explain that on their turn, they can put down another 8 (above or below the 8 you placed) or the number that is one more or one less than that number (to the right or the left of your 8).

- The child next to that person looks at his or her card. If it is a 7, 8 or 9, the student can place a card. Otherwise the student says, "Fiddle faddle." Mark a tally on your chart for every fiddle faddle.

- On the second turn, if a player puts down a 7, the next player plays a 6, 7, 8, or 9. (The first time you play, you may need to help students with the one more, one less rule.) Continue going around the circle until time is up or all students have placed their cards.

- At the end of the game, figure out how many "fiddle faddles" it took to sort all the cards.

K

Growing Pattern Songs

NCTM Content Standard:

Algebra

NCTM Process Standard:

Reasoning & Proof

Specific math content or skill addressed:

Patterns

Component:

Activity

Materials needed:

Chart of song lyrics

Preparing students for success:

Be sure students have plenty of time to sing and enjoy the song(s) before making any tie-in to math.

Students should already have developed a strong beginning understanding of basic repeating patterns.

Because these songs are somewhat long, it might take several days or time periods to complete this activity. You may want to teach two or three verses a day.

Vocabulary:

Pattern

How to do it:

- Display a song chart and teach students the words to a "cumulative" song. In mathematical terms, these songs have "growing patterns," but students do not need to know this term right away.

- Sing the song through several times so that students get the melody.

- Invite students to add movements for various sections or lines of the song. For instance, if you sing the song "Today is Monday" with students, they might suggest movements like these:

Today is Monday,	(hold up one finger for first day of week)
Monday wash day,	(act like you are washing)
All you hungry people,	(pretend to cram food in your mouth)
We wish the same to you.	(hold out hands with an open gesture)
Today is Tuesday,	(hold up two fingers)
Tuesday string beans,	(make an icky face—students do not always like green beans)
Monday wash day,	(act like you are washing)
All you hungry people,	(pretend to cram food in your mouth)
We wish the same to you.	(hold out hands with an open gesture)
Today is Wednesday,	(hold up three fingers)
Wednesday soup,	(pretend to eat with a spoon)
Tuesday string beans,	(make an icky face)
Monday wash day,	(act like you are washing)
All you hungry people,	(pretend to cram food in your mouth)
We wish the same to you.	(hold out hands with an open gesture)
Today is Thursday,	(hold up four fingers)
Thursday roast beef,	(pretend to hold up big fork)
Wednesday soup,	(pretend to eat with a spoon)
Tuesday string beans,	(make an icky face)
Monday wash day,	(act like you are washing)
All you hungry people,	(pretend to cram food in your mouth)
We wish the same to you.	(hold out hands with an open gesture)
Today is Friday,	(hold up five fingers)
Friday fish,	(put hands together like a fish swimming)
Thursday roast beef,	(pretend to hold up big fork)
Wednesday soup,	(pretend to eat with a spoon)
Tuesday string beans,	(make an icky face)
Monday wash day,	(act like you are washing)
All you hungry people,	(pretend to cram food in your mouth)
We wish the same to you.	(hold out hands with an open gesture)

Today is Saturday,	(hold up six fingers)
Saturday payday,	(rub your fingers together like you are receiving money)
Friday fish,	(put hands together like a fish swimming)
Thursday roast beef,	(pretend to hold up big fork)
Wednesday soup,	(pretend to eat with a spoon)
Tuesday string beans,	(make an icky face)
Monday wash day,	(act like you are washing)
All you hungry people,	(pretend to cram food in your mouth)
We wish the same to you.	(hold out hands with an open gesture)
Today is Sunday,	(hold up seven fingers)
Sunday rest,	(put hands together and rest side of head on side of hands)
Saturday payday,	(rub your fingers together like you are receiving money)
Friday fish,	(put hands together like a fish swimming)
Thursday roast beef,	(pretend to hold up big fork)
Wednesday soup,	(pretend to eat with a spoon)
Tuesday string beans,	(make an icky face)
Monday wash day,	(act like you are washing)
All you hungry people,	(pretend to cram food in your mouth)
We wish the same to you.	(hold out hands with an open gesture)

■ Ask students what they noticed about the song. Take a variety of comments. If no one mentions the pattern, ask, *"Is there a pattern to this song? What is it?"* Possible student responses include:

❋ *"Yes, it's a pattern because it repeats."*

❋ *"No, it's not a pattern because it is not the same every time."*

❋ *"It adds something every time."*

❋ *"Well, it's sort of the same and sort of different every time, so I don't know."*

VARIATION:

Some other songs or chants that show growing patterns include "There Was an Old Lady Who Swallowed a Fly," "Mother Gooney Bird," and "The Button Factory." (See the book *Energizers!: 88 Quick Movement Activities That Refresh and Refocus, K–6* for more details.)

EXTENSIONS DURING A LATER MATH LESSON:

■ Remind students about the song. Let students know that the song actually has a kind of pattern called a growing pattern. Talk about growing patterns, if possible, using the same terminology they used earlier in the day.

■ Show a simple growing pattern with math manipulatives: ABABBABBB. Continue building the pattern by asking students *"What comes next?"*

I Spy a Shape

NCTM Content Standard:

Geometry

NCTM Process Standard:

Problem Solving,
Communication,
Connections

**Specific math content
or skill addressed:**

Identifying shapes

Component:

Activity

Materials needed:

None

**Preparing students
for success:**

Playing I Spy the traditional
way with students will help
prepare them for this game.

Students should have some
familiarity with some basic
shapes: squares, circles,
hexagons, trapezoids,
rectangles, spheres,
cubes, and cylinders.

Vocabulary:

Squares, circles, hexagons,
trapezoids, rectangles,
spheres, cubes, cylinders

How to do it:

■ Let students know that they are going to play I Spy a little differently today. The person who is the "spy" will look for a shape in the classroom but will not identify it to the group. The "spy" will say *"I spy with my little eye a _____ _____."* The student will fill in the blank with the name of a shape and its size or color. For instance, a student might say *"I spy with my little eye a clear square"* to identify a window pane or *"I spy with my little eye a giant rectangle"* to identify a ceiling tile. Be sure students understand that they should only choose shapes visible to everyone. (Students might know, for example, that the pattern block box contains a yellow hexagon, but if it can't be seen from the circle, it's off limits.)

■ Randomly select a spy.

■ Students who think they know the secret shape raise their hands, and the spy calls on a few. If after three or four guesses, no one has named the shape, the spy identifies it.

■ Repeat the process several times.

VARIATIONS:

■ As students get more experienced with this game, ask them to use properties other than size and color to describe their shapes.

■ This game can also be played when working on numbers. The spy identifies by number similar objects located together in the classroom and visible from the circle. For instance, the spy might say *"I see three"* after seeing three cabinet doors in a row. The other students use the number to guess what the spy sees.

Lines, Lines Everywhere

NCTM Content Standard:

Geometry

NCTM Process Standard:

Connections

**Specific math content
or skill addressed:**

Line segments,
identifying shapes

Component:

Morning message

Materials needed:

Colored masking tape
or long thin strips of
construction paper

Message chart (for the
morning message)

**Preparing students
for success:**

This message works
particularly well after you
have discussed lines in math
or other contexts (like visual
art). It can work with no prior
discussion, but students will
get more out of it if they
have some familiarity with
lines and their role in
geometry and art.

Vocabulary:

Line, shape names

How to do it:

■ Post some version of the message
to the right.

■ Before Morning Meeting, each
student adds one long piece of
tape or construction paper to the
message chart in order to create
an abstract design. You will need
to decide if you want them to cut
their own strips. If so, you may
want to include some guidance in
the message about how long those
should be (about the length of their
forearms works well). If not, you'll
need to have strips and/or glue
sticks ready.

> Dear Artists,
>
> In Art we looked at lines.
> We will make pictures
> with lines. Put a tape line
> here to make a picture.

■ During the message portion of the meeting, ask students to look at the
design they created. You might ask *"What do you see in it?"* or *"What
do you notice?"* Students may respond by pointing out certain shapes that
intersecting lines make or by saying something about the lines (*"They are
all going in the same direction." "These two are crashing into each other."
"These two look like part of a square."*) If students do not respond, ask
them questions that will focus them on shapes and/or lines in the picture.
For instance, you might ask *"What shapes can you find in our picture?"*
or *"What do you notice about the lines in our picture?"*

VARIATION:

For a greeting, lay a large piece of paper in the center of the circle. Students
should choose someone to greet who is not sitting directly next to them. Lay
a piece of tape on the paper between all the pairs who greet. After everyone
has greeted someone, the class analyzes the lines and shapes using the same
structure outlined earlier.

EXTENSION DURING A LATER MATH LESSON:

Have students each make their own line art using long pieces of construction paper, straws, or colored masking tape. Later, students exchange papers
and see what kinds of shapes and/or lines they can find in their partners'
artwork.

Number Lineup

NCTM Content Standard:

Number & Operations

NCTM Process Standard:

Reasoning & Proof

**Specific math content
or skill addressed:**

Counting, identifying
numbers

Component:

Activity

Materials needed:

Number cards beginning
with 1 and continuing to the
number of students you have

**Preparing students
for success:**

Students need to be fairly
adept at counting and
recognizing numerals.
(If you have a few students
who struggle with these
concepts, you can still play
the game—just be sure to
give them lower numerals.)

Vocabulary:

Least, greatest,
numeral names

How to do it:

- Shuffle the numeral cards thoroughly. Give each student a numeral card. (Do not pass them out in numerical order, as doing so will remove the fun and challenge of the game.)

- At your signal, students line up in the order of their numbers as quickly as they can.

- Once students get in numerical order, have them count from least to greatest.

- Then, pretend to be the north wind, blow on them, and have them "mess up" their line so they are no longer in order but are still in line. (You should model how to safely and carefully move when blown by the wind.)

- Have students switch numbers with someone close to them and signal them to line up in order again.

- Have the north wind blow again so that students "shuffle themselves."

- Challenge students to count down starting with the highest number. Once they say their number, they should sit down in the circle.

- Now let students know you are all going to count by twos. As you count by twos, the students whose numbers are called stand up and line up in order. Then, have them count down and sit down in the circle.

- Tell students you will now help everyone count by twos in a different way. Start at one and count by twos as the students with the number cards you call stand up and line up in order. Then, have them count down and sit down in the circle.

VARIATIONS:

- After the students have lined up in order, place a string down the center of the circle and have students put their number cards in order like a number line. Then, students use a die to move a marker (like a math manipulative or a small stuffed animal) up or down on the number line. You could do this in an around-the-circle fashion. Students announce before they roll whether the marker should be moved up or down. Each student rolls the die, then makes the marker hop that number of spaces up or down on the number line.

- Later in the year, as students become familiar with larger numbers, give out cards with numbers that are spread out (2, 7, 15, 21, etc.) and ask students to put themselves in order from least to greatest. Also ask students to sort themselves in certain ways ("*If your number has a 2, stand in this hoop,*" etc.)

EXTENSION DURING A LATER MATH LESSON:

As a center or small group activity, give students a set of shuffled number cards to put in order. Individualize this activity depending upon the numbers on which a given student is working.

Number Line Walk

NCTM Content Standard:

Number & Operations

NCTM Process Standard:

Problem Solving

Specific math content or skill addressed:

Counting, number relationships

Component:

Activity

Materials needed:

One die

Large paper number line with spaces big enough for student to step on (see example to the right)

Preparing students for success:

Students should have prior experience with counting and number relationships.

Before beginning the activity, inform students that not everyone will actually get to walk on the number line, but everyone will get to play by rolling a die or counting aloud.

Vocabulary:

Names of numbers, how many more

| 20 |
| 19 |
| 18 |
| 17 |
| 16 |
| 15 |
| 14 |
| 13 |
| 12 |
| 11 |
| 10 |
| 9 |
| 8 |
| 7 |
| 6 |
| 5 |
| 4 |
| 3 |
| 2 |
| 1 |
| 0 |

How to do it:

■ Let the class know that the goal of this game is to see how quickly the class can get to the highest number on the number line. (The highest number should fit what the class is studying—for example, if you're working on the numbers 0 to 20, the highest number should be 20.)

■ Randomly select a student to be the first "number line walker." That student stands on zero.

■ Select another student to roll the die.

■ The number line walker walks that number of spaces as classmates count aloud. The class identifies the number the walker landed on.

■ Randomly select a new number line walker to go stand on that space.

■ Continue rolls until the number line walker makes it to the "top" of the number line (or past it).

■ Repeat, as time permits, with several other students taking turns walking and rolling.

■ When you get close to the end of the number line, ask students questions like *"How many more spaces will it be until we get to _____? How could we find out?"*

VARIATIONS:

■ This game can be played with a one more/one less die. (You can make this either by writing on a blank cube with a marker or putting circle labels on a regular die and writing on the labels. The die should have three sides with "one more" and three sides with "one less.") The number line walker starts in the middle of the line and ends up either at zero or the top number.

■ Instead of allowing the walker to go past the top of the number line, challenge the class to hit the top number exactly.

EXTENSION DURING A LATER MATH LESSON:

Have students (especially those who did not have a turn at walking on the number line in Morning Meeting) play the activity with a partner. One partner rolls the die and the other counts the spaces on the line. The partners switch roles once the walker reaches the end of the number line.

Numbers in My House

NCTM Content Standard:
Number & Operations

NCTM Process Standard:
Connections, Communication

**Specific math content
or skill addressed:**
Identifying numbers,
number relationships

Component:
Sharing

Materials needed:
Objects students bring from home

**Preparing students
for success:**

A day or so before the share, ask students to bring one object that contains numbers from their homes. The object should be small and not too valuable. Give a few examples—a can from the kitchen, a cheap watch, an old phone. (Depending upon school rules or your own preferences, you may need to specify whether toys are included.)

Be prepared to let students who forgot or could not find anything choose something from the classroom. To make this more special, consider letting them look through some items they might not ordinarily get to see (from your cabinets, etc.)

Vocabulary:

Terms will vary depending upon what students share. If you do the sorting portion of the sharing, you will use terms such as grouping, similar, or alike.

How to do it:

- When it is time for Morning Meeting, direct all students to bring their objects but to place them behind themselves in the circle.

- At sharing time, give students a sentence frame: *"I brought a _____ because _____."* Model how to show the object and the numbers in or on it. For instance, you might say *"I brought a favorite book of recipes because it has numbers to tell you how much to put into what you are making."*

- Let one or two students practice as you modeled. Help them use the sentence frame and think about what purpose the numbers on their objects serve.

- When you are sure everyone understands the structure, go around the circle and let everyone share.

- Ask students *"Did you see any ways that we could group some of the objects people brought? Did anyone have things that were similar or alike?"* Sort the objects in several different ways as time permits.

VARIATIONS:

- Using the morning message, direct students to look for things in the room that have numbers and to be ready to talk about them at the meeting (instead of bringing them).

- As you introduce or focus on various numbers with students, you could limit the sharing to one particular number. For example: *"Find something with the number 5 on it."*

EXTENSION DURING A LATER MATH LESSON:

Have the students write about or draw a picture of what they brought, and combine the pictures and writing into a class book.

Odd or Even

NCTM Content Standard:

Number & Operations

NCTM Process Standard:

Reasoning & Proof

**Specific math content
or skill addressed:**

Odd & even

Component:

Activity

Materials needed:

Music

Number cards (0 to 10)

**Preparing students
for success:**

Model and practice what safe
and appropriate movement
in the center of the circle
looks and sounds like.

Model and practice how to
find partners quickly and
safely. Also, explain to the
students that they may
not always have a partner
in this game.

Vocabulary:

Odd, even

How to do it:

■ Shuffle the number cards. Select a number and randomly choose that many students to come to the center of the circle. Let them know that they can dance or move around to the music, but when the music stops, they should find the closest person among those in the center of the circle to be a partner.

■ Play the music. When it stops, wait for students to find partners. Reinforce safe movement and kindness towards others. (Sample statements: *"I notice everyone is having fun dancing but also keeping hands and feet to themselves." "I saw most people find the closest person to be a partner without worrying about who it was." "I saw so many friendly faces when you were looking for partners—that must have made everyone feel special."*)

■ The students still in the circle notice whether everyone in the center has a partner or not. If everyone does have a partner, guide the students to note that the number is even. If not, guide them to note that the number is odd. You might even want to record these observations for later use.

■ Continue playing with different numbers and students, trying to make sure all students have about the same number of chances to be in the middle. A student who doesn't have a partner can draw the next card.

■ After a few rounds, start asking students still sitting in the circle to predict whether the number of students in the center is odd or even before you play music and have students pair up.

VARIATION:

Once students are familiar with the game, use two cards at once. Note whether the numbers on the cards are odd or even and then randomly select that many students to go the center of the circle to try to find partners. After students find partners, note whether the resulting number is odd or even. For instance, if you draw a 2 and a 10, students will note that these two numbers are even. After all twelve students in the center find partners, observe that two even numbers added together make an even number.

EXTENSION DURING A LATER MATH LESSON:

Do a similar activity using number cards, counters, and a recording sheet. Students draw a number card and count out that many counters. Then, they pair up the counters. They record whether that number is odd or even. Students who need an extra challenge should use the addition version of the game, drawing two cards each time.

Grade Level

K

Patterns Around the Circle

NCTM Content Standard:

Algebra

NCTM Process Standard:

Problem Solving,
Communication,
Connections

**Specific math content
or skill addressed:**

Patterns

Component:

Activity

Materials needed:

None

**Preparing students
for success:**

This activity is very lively and
exciting, so be sure students
are proficient at responding
to signals for attention.

Vocabulary:

Pattern

How to do it:

■ Give students a simple pattern consisting of two movements such as *hop, clap*. Practice the pattern in the circle with the class.

■ When students seem to have the hang of the pattern, have everyone make a half turn to the right and perform the pattern simultaneously. Call out the pattern as you do it: *"Hop, clap, hop, clap."*

■ Repeat with other movements or more complex patterns.

VARIATIONS:

■ Once students have become adept at patterning, call out the symbolic representation for the pattern as you do it. For instance, instead of *"Hop, clap, hop, clap,"* call out *"A, B, A, B."*

■ Make a die with various movements on it. For instance, the sides could be step, hop, clap, pat, snap, tiptoe. To figure out the pattern, have a student roll the movement die and then roll a number die to determine the first part of the pattern. Then have another student roll the movement die and the number die to figure out the next part of the pattern. For instance, the resulting pattern could be *"2 steps, 3 hops."*

EXTENSION DURING A LATER MATH LESSON:

Use picture cards corresponding to movements. (For example, you might have a walking card, a hopping card, a clapping card, and so on.) Students use these to make their own patterns, and you can try them out at later Morning Meetings.

Plus/Minus

NCTM Content Standard:
Number & Operations

NCTM Process Standard:
Problem Solving

Specific math content or skill addressed:
Addition, subtraction

Component:
Activity

Materials needed:
One +/– die

One regular die

Blocks, pattern blocks, or some other manipulatives

Preparing students for success:
Students should have some general familiarity with the plus and minus symbols, i.e. that plus means adding two or more numbers and minus means the difference between two numbers.

Students should have had experience with whatever material you use for the building or design aspect of this activity.

Some students may get attached to the particular pieces they add to the class structure. Be sure to explain to them that their pieces may be taken away.

Vocabulary:
Plus, minus, more, less, add, subtract or take away

How to do it:

- Before Morning Meeting, make a design or build a structure in the center of the circle using some of the manipulatives you have chosen (use about twenty pieces). You may want to count and record how many you used at the beginning so students can compare that to how many you have at the end. Students also may enjoy before/after digital photos.

- Explain to students that, on their turn, they will each roll the +/– die and the regular die. (If you do not have a +/– die, you can make one by writing on a blank cube with a marker or putting circle labels on a regular die and writing on the labels. The die should have three sides with the + symbol and three sides with a – symbol.)

- If they get a +, they will add that number of blocks. If they get a –, they will take that many away. Tell them that when they are adding or subtracting blocks, they should try to make an interesting design or structure.

- As students take their turns, encourage them to verbalize their rolls by saying something like *"I rolled plus 3. That means I am going to add three blocks."*

- At the end, see how many blocks in all you have. Compare that to the number with which you started.

VARIATION:

Use whatever materials you have to start a small town. Start by building several small buildings throughout the center of the circle. On each turn, the students add new buildings, make the buildings taller, make them shorter, or make them disappear.

EXTENSION DURING A LATER MATH LESSON:

This is a fun game for students to play with partners or at a center. If you have students who need a challenge, have them play this game by recording numerically what happens on each turn.

Shoe Graph

NCTM Content Standard:

Data Analysis & Probability,
Number & Operations

NCTM Process Standard:

Reasoning & Proof,
Communication

**Specific math content
or skill addressed:**

Graphs & diagrams, counting

Component:

Activity

Materials needed:

None

**Preparing students
for success:**

Students should have
developed enough self-
control that they can do an
activity with their shoes
calmly and safely.

It's especially fun to do this
activity after doing the Shoe
Twister Greeting (see *99
Activities and Greetings*).
Students could just keep
one shoe off and place
it behind them during
sharing time.

Vocabulary:

Sort, least, most, graph

How to do it:

- In the circle, ask students to take off one of their shoes and place it in front of them. Tell them everyone is going to sort the shoes in a certain way.

- Direct them to listen to the categories you call out. Possibilities include color of shoes, fastener (Velcro, ties, slip-ons), and type of shoe (sneaker, flip flop, dress shoe). Begin with a category that includes only a small number of students. For example, ask all students with pink shoes to stand and pick up their shoes.

- Direct the students in the first category to line their shoes up in a straight line in the middle of the circle. Help with this as necessary.

- Ask students in the next category (for instance, brown shoes) to stand and pick up their shoes. Direct them to place their shoes in a new line below the first. They should line up the shoes to fit in a one-to-one pattern with the first line.

- Continue the process until you have exhausted all categories.

- Ask students to look at the shoe graph and tell you *"Which kind of shoe do we have most of? Which kind of shoe do we have least of? Are there any lines that have the same or an equal amount?"*

EXTENSIONS DURING A LATER MATH LESSON:

- Have students work together to graph some other aspects of themselves (hair, eye color, etc.)

- Students with enough experience with graphs should create their own graphs by designing and asking classmates certain questions, then recording the results.

Shorter/Longer

How to do it:

NCTM Content Standard:

Measurement

NCTM Process Standard:

Connections, Communication, Reasoning & Proof

Specific math content or skill addressed:

Comparison, measurement, counting

Component:

Morning message

Materials needed:

Objects from the classroom

Message chart (for the morning message)

Preparing students for success:

Students need to have some familiarity and practice with the words and concepts of "shorter than" and "longer than."

Vocabulary:

Shorter than, longer than, shortest, longest

- Include some version of the example to the right as a related task on your message. (Be ready to have students measuring your feet all morning! Or leave an extra shoe near the chart.)

- During the message portion of the meeting, have students reflect on the check marks. For instance, you might ask *"Which has more—shorter than or longer than? . . . Which has less? . . . Let's count and see."*

- Ask a few students to retrieve the objects they used. Begin placing objects in a row from shortest to longest.

> Find one object in our classroom. Is it shorter or longer than my shoe? Put a check on our chart:
>
> Shorter   Longer
> than   than

VARIATION:

Use this activity to work on other concepts. You might ask students to find things that are taller than or shorter than or wider than or thinner than. For weight, you might ask students to find objects that are heavier than or lighter than a given object.

EXTENSION DURING A LATER MATH LESSON:

Ask students to do the same activity at math time and order a set of objects from shortest to longest, then draw or write about their objects.

Grade Level

K

Skip Greeting

NCTM Content Standard:

Number & Operations

NCTM Process Standard:

Problem Solving

**Specific math content
or skill addressed:**

Counting, number
relationships

Component:

Greeting

Materials needed:

None

**Preparing students
for success:**

Students should have
mastered the basics of
friendly greetings.

Vocabulary:

Ordinal and cardinal
numbers

How to do it:

■ Choose the target number you will "skip by." Write that number on the board or chart both numerically and with a dot representation (like the face of a die).

■ All students stand in the circle.

■ The first student counts the number of people represented by the target number.

■ She greets the next person. For instance, if the target number is two, she counts two classmates and greets the third person in the circle.

■ The student who was counting and greeting sits down.

■ The person who was greeted then counts the target number among those still standing, greets the next person and sits down, and so forth.

■ Students who are seated should not be counted but can be acknowledged with a friendly face.

So Does Mine

NCTM Content Standard:

Number & Operations

NCTM Process Standard:

Reasoning & Proof

Specific math content or skill addressed:

Money, sorting/grouping, attribution

Component:

Activity

Materials needed:

One coin for each student (a mix of pennies, nickels, dimes, and quarters)

Preparing students for success:

Students may do better with this game if they have previously played social games with similar directions like Just Like Me (see *99 Activities and Greetings*).

Students should have some familiarity with coins.

Make sure students know that it is okay if a person next to them or anywhere in the circle makes a mistake and sits or stands at the wrong time. They do not need to correct that person.

Vocabulary:

Penny, nickel, dime, quarter, cents, face, heads, tails

How to do it:

■ Give each student a coin. Let them know that you will say something about a coin like *"My coin is round."* If what you say is true of their coin, they should stand up and say *"Mine is, too!"* If it is not true, they should quietly stay seated.

■ Some statements you might make include the following (but not necessarily in this order):

❊ *"My coin is silver (or copper)."*

❊ *"My coin has a smooth (or ridged) edge."*

❊ *"My coin is worth _____ cent(s)."*

❊ *"My coin has the face of _____."*

❊ *"My coin has the number ____."*

❊ *"My coin has the word _____."*

❊ *"My coin is the thickest (or thinnest)."*

❊ *"My coin is shiny (or dull)."*

❊ *"Let's put our coins in our palms. My coin is now heads side up."*

■ At the end of the game, see if students can figure out some questions that would leave no one standing, one person standing, or everyone standing. For instance, a student might suggest saying *"My coin is the dirtiest one in the circle."* Or, a student thinking at a fairly high level might suggest that you pick a specific date and see whose coin has that date.

VARIATIONS:

■ Assign or have students find partners. When you make the statements this time, the partners stand if the statements are true. Statements you might include for partners would be:

❊ *"My partner and I have the same (or different) coins."*

❊ *"My partner's coin and my coin add up to _____ cents."*

CONTINUED

So Does Mine CONTINUED

    ✳ *"My partner's coin and my coin are both silver (or different colors)."*

    ✳ *"My partner's coin and my coin both have the number ____."*

■ Go around the circle and let students say one thing about their coin. Any students whose coins have a similar feature stand up and say *"Mine does, too."*

EXTENSION DURING A LATER MATH LESSON:

Use this activity as a warm-up lesson for math time. Give students (or pairs of students) baggies or sets of coins. Let them sort the coins according to some of the attributes used in the game.

String Shapes

NCTM Content Standard:

Geometry

NCTM Process Standard:

Problem Solving,
Communication

**Specific math content
or skill addressed:**

Identifying shapes

Component:

Activity

Materials needed:

Loops of yarn about two
yards or two meters long,
enough for trios or pairs
of students

**Preparing students
for success:**

Students need to have
some prior experience
and knowledge of shapes
and their attributes.

Students need to have
some practice working
with partners.

You will need to assign
partners or have a random
way of assigning partners
before this activity.

Vocabulary:

Corners, sides, square,
rectangle, triangle

How to do it:

- Students should be in groups of two or three.

- Give each group a loop of yarn.

- Challenge each group to work together to use its yarn to make a triangle. Circulate and reinforce students' teamwork and/or mathematical thinking. *("I see you found a way for each of you to hold one corner of the triangle— that way, everyone gets to participate." "I see three sides and three corners—that is definitely a triangle!")*

- Challenge groups to make different types of triangles. As you circulate among groups, use questions or comments to push their thinking about this task if necessary. Many kindergartners will produce an equilateral triangle (a triangle with three equal sides) and may modify it only slightly on the second challenge. They may need some assistance envisioning or creating a completely different type of triangle. For instance, you might ask some of these questions:

  ✳ *"What would happen if you made one side really long?"*

  ✳ *"Can you figure out a way to make one of the corners look like the corner of a square or rectangle?"*

  ✳ *"Can you find a way to make two sides the same, but not the other one?"*

- Challenge groups to come up with a shape that has four sides. Make some observations quickly about what you see. *("I see three groups have made squares, four groups have made rectangles, and one group has made a shape we haven't talked about yet. We'll come back to that.")*

- Now challenge the group to create another but different four-sided shape. Again, be ready to make observations or ask questions to encourage students to think more deeply if necessary. Here are some examples of what you might say:

  ✳ *"I noticed all of your corners are square corners. Can you find a way to make one of them different? Maybe you could make it look like one of the corners on your triangle."*

  ✳ *"What would happen if you made one of your sides really short or long?"*

  ✳ *"Can you find a way to make the red pattern block shape?"*

CONTINUED

35

String Shapes

■ Give students time to create a shape of their choice, but circulate and help any group that has trouble agreeing on a final shape.

VARIATIONS:

■ Use one large string and call on several students to create shapes according to your directions. Have the rest of the class watch and notice.

■ Give sets of partners a geoboard and large rubber band. Challenge them to come up with certain shapes or shapes that meet certain specifications.

EXTENSION DURING A LATER MATH LESSON:

This is a great activity to use before a lesson with geoboards. If any groups came up with shapes you had not yet discussed in class, take a few minutes and discuss the attributes of those shapes. Compare them with shapes students already know or are familiar with.

Grade Level

K

Time to . . .

NCTM Content Standard:

Measurement

NCTM Process Standard:

Connections

Specific math content or skill addressed:

Time

Component:

Activity

Materials needed:

Large demonstration clock with movable hands

Chart (optional)

Preparing students for success:

Students should have some familiarity with telling time to the hour.

If you use the "changing seats" activity, be sure to model and practice safe, friendly and quick ways to find a new seat.

Vocabulary:

Minute hand, hour hand, o'clock

How to do it:

- Let students know that in this game the clock is wild and might land on any time. When it does land on a time, they will have to say what time it is and complete certain tasks.

- Begin with four times—12:00, 3:00, 6:00, 9:00. You can either assign an activity for each of these times or take input from students as to what they might do at those times. Here are some examples of activities that you might have them do:

  ❋ 3:00   time to go home—everyone turns and sits with back to the center of the circle

  ❋ 6:00   time to eat dinner—everyone mimics eating a meal

  ❋ 9:00   time to go to bed—everyone lies down on his or her spot

  ❋ 12:00   time to switch places—everyone has to find a new seat in the circle quickly and safely

- If it would help the class, post a chart with icons for what to do for each time.

- Move the minute hand of the clock around. As you do so, you might have students move their hands in the same direction or say a little rhyme (*"Around and around goes the minute hand, watch and see where it will land"*). When you get to one of the times, stop and say *"What time is it?"* Students should respond *"It is ___ o'clock—time to _____."* (Students do not need to be exact about what they say. For instance, if it's 6:00, they might just say *"It is time to eat,"* or some might say *"It's time for dinner."* Both would be acceptable.) Then, they should act out whatever is appropriate for that time.

- Repeat several times.

VARIATIONS:

- Have students play this game in slow or fast motion.

- As students become more adept with following the directions of this game, add activities for more times of day.

37

Under the Cup

NCTM Content Standard:

Number & Operations

NCTM Process Standard:

Problem Solving

Specific math content or skill addressed:

Counting, number relationships

Component:

Activity

Materials needed:

Ten nontransparent cups (numbered 1–10 on bottoms of cups)

One small object (penny, cube, etc.)

Preparing students for success:

Students should have experience with counting and numbers to ten.

Vocabulary:

More than, less than, higher than, lower than

How to do it:

- Put the cups upside down in numerical order in the center of the circle. Students stand up and slowly circle the cups until everyone has seen the written numerals right-side-up.

- Have students turn their backs or close their eyes. While the students' eyes are closed, hide an object under one of the cups.

- Randomly select a student to guess where the object is.

- If the guess is incorrect, give students clues about where the object is in relation to the cup the student guessed. For instance, if a student guessed "four" and the object is under the cup marked 6, you might say *"No, the penny is under a cup that is more than (or higher than) four."*

- Continue taking guesses until students find the object.

- Repeat several times.

VARIATIONS:

- Once you have played several times, start letting students hide the object and help you give clues.

- When students become adept with numbers higher than ten, add cups 11–20, then 21–30.

EXTENSION DURING A LATER MATH LESSON:

If students work well independently, have them play this game as partners at math or center time.

Grade Level

K

Yes/No Questions

NCTM Content Standard:

Number & Operations, Algebra

NCTM Process Standard:

Problem Solving, Communication, Connections

Specific math content or skill addressed:

Counting, comparison, algebra

Component:

Morning message

Materials needed:

Student name labels on reusable adhesive

Message chart (for the morning message)

Preparing students for success:

Before you use this activity for the first time, model how to place a name label in the appropriate spot on the message chart.

Vocabulary:

More, less, how many, how many more, how many fewer

How to do it:

■ Include a yes-or-no question as a related task on your message. Here are a few possibilities:

✳ *Do you like to draw pictures?*

✳ *Do you like to ride bikes?*

✳ *Do you like to get your lunch from the cafeteria?*

✳ *Did you like yesterday's story?*

✳ *Would you like to meet _____?*

■ As students come into the class, they should read the question or message (perhaps with help from picture clues or help from you), then remove their name labels from the location in which they are kept and place them under "yes" or "no."

■ During the message portion of the meeting, direct students' attention to the question. Line up the labels under the "yes" column and the labels under the "no" column in straight vertical lines next to each other. There should be one "yes" corresponding to each "no" until you reach the point where one group is more than the other. After completion, the two lines will look like a graph.

■ Lead the students to analyze the results by asking some of these questions:

✳ *"Which has more (or less) — yes or no?"*

✳ *"How many students answered 'yes'? How many students answered 'no'?"* Either lead the whole group in counting, or call on individual students and have them explain how they figured out the total.

✳ *"How many more students answered yes than no* (or vice versa)*?"* Lead students in counting the "extra" labels.

✳ *"How many people are here today?"* Again, you can either lead the whole group to calculate the total, or later in the year, ask for individuals to figure it out and explain their thinking.

CONTINUED

39

✳ A more advanced question might be *"If our class has ___ people and ___ people are here, how many people are missing?"* Lead students to count up from the number present to the number of people in the class.

VARIATION:

This structure also works for questions with two choices for answers. For instance: *"Which kind of sandwich do you like better—peanut butter and jelly or turkey and cheese?"*

K

Zero Sharing

NCTM Content Standard:
Number & Operations

NCTM Process Standard:
Communication

Specific math content or skill addressed:
Mathematical description

Component:
Sharing

Materials needed:
Chart

Preparing students for success:
Students need to have some familiarity with the number zero (or whatever number is being used).

Vocabulary:
Zero (or whatever other number you are working with)

How to do it:

■ Let students know that everyone will share about something they would like to have zero of. Model a complete but brief sentence such as *"I would like to have zero smelly diapers"* or *"I would like to have zero ice cream cones with ketchup on top."* If appropriate, write the sentence starter on a chart. You may also want to brainstorm some ideas first.

■ Go around the circle and guide students through the sharing.

■ You may want to record students' ideas for future use.

VARIATIONS:

■ Use other numbers. To make sure students are really considering the meaning of these numbers, use limiting language such as *"I would like two, but only two, _____."*

■ Read the book *Zero is the Leaves on the Tree* by Betsy Franco before or after this sharing.

EXTENSION DURING A LATER MATH LESSON:

If you recorded the students' ideas, type them up or let students write them out. Have students illustrate each idea with a lift-the-flap picture under the typed or written text.

41

Adding Our Way to 100

NCTM Content Standard:

Number & Operations

NCTM Process Standard:

Problem Solving,
Communication

**Specific math content
or skill addressed:**

Addition, counting

Component:

Activity

Materials needed:

Number cards (0–10),
four of each card

Large paper version of
a hundreds chart

Markers or crayons

**Preparing students
for success:**

Students should have
experience with addition.

Students will need partners
for this activity. Choose a
quick way of selecting these.
(For instance, your partner is
the person sitting to your
right, your partner is the
person you greeted, etc.)

Vocabulary:

How many, total, how many
more, less than, more than

How to do it:

- Tape the hundreds chart to a chart so that it is visible to all students in the circle.

- Shuffle and place the number cards face down in front of the chart stand or in the middle of the circle.

- Let students know that the goal of this activity is to see how many cards it takes to get to 100. (Due to time constraints, it's probably best not to try to hit 100 exactly, so going past 100 is okay.)

- Randomly select one student to come forward and turn over two cards.

- Ask students to work with a partner to figure out the total of the two cards. (Have manipulatives available, if necessary.) Call on a pair to share their sum and explain how they figured it out.

- Randomly select another student to come forward and color that many squares on the hundreds chart. Use a different colored crayon or marker to color the chart for each turn.

- Repeat the process until you get close to 100. Keep the pace brisk, but if you have not reached 100 in about five to ten minutes, you could stop the game in the middle and continue it as a warm-up at math time.

- As you get close (within twelve or so of 100), spur student thinking by asking some questions like these:

  ✳ *"How many more do we need to color to reach 100? How did you figure that out?"* For instance, if all the squares up to and including 90 had been colored, possible student responses include:

    ✎ *"It is ten—I just counted by ones."*

    ✎ *"I know it is ten because the 90 is right above the 100, and on a hundreds chart, you count down by tens."*

    ✎ *"I know it is ten because when we count by tens, we go 10, 20, 30, 40, 50, 60, 70, 80, 90, 100."*

  ✳ *"Which cards could we turn over that would make that number?"*

  ✳ *"Which cards could we turn over that would make us have less than 100?"*

CONTINUED ▶

If you have students who are performing well above grade level, you could also occasionally ask these questions during earlier rounds of the game as a challenge.

■ Once you have colored all the squares to 100, ask students to look at the chart and figure out how many turns it took to get to 100. As a challenge, ask students *"How many cards did we use in all? How did you figure that out?"*

VARIATION:

Play this game with dice. Choose a number by which the class will skip count. Select a student randomly to roll the die. Skip count that many squares and have a student color the squares on which you land. For instance, if the skip counting number is one, and a student rolls a three, the student colors 2, 4, and 6. On the next turn, if a student rolls a four, that student colors 8, 10, 12, and 14. At the end of the game, you could see what students notice about the pattern as a result.

EXTENSION DURING A LATER MATH LESSON:

Have students play this game with partners at math time. The partners can share a blank chart and take turns turning over cards and coloring in squares. Have partners record number sentences (like 6 + 2 = 8) for their sums.

Beanbag Toss

How to do it:

- Select a certain number of beanbags to use in the game depending upon where students are mathematically.

- Place the hoop or large piece of paper in the center of the circle.

- Give one beanbag to each of several students around the circle. On a given signal, they all gently toss their beanbags toward the hoop or paper.

- The class counts how many landed in or out (or on or off). Lead them to connect those amounts with the total number of beanbags. You might say, for example, *"So, three in and four out makes seven, or 3 + 4 = 7."*

- Record the results on a chart like the example to the right.

- Continue playing a few more rounds, giving all students at least one chance to toss.

- Encourage students to think more about this activity by asking some or all of these questions:

IN	OUT
3	4
0	7
2	5
2	5
3	4
2	5

  ❋ *"What do you notice about our results?"* Possible student answers include:

  ✏ *"We usually got more out than in."*

  ✏ *"Some throws were the same."*

  ✏ *"We had two in a row that were the same."*

  ❋ *"Are there other ways to make seven besides these ways?"*

VARIATION:

Instead of recording on a table, record each turn as a number sentence (like 3 + 4 = 7, 5 + 2 = 7).

EXTENSION DURING A LATER MATH LESSON:

Have the students play this game individually using small counters. They place the counters in a small container and spill them onto a small piece of paper on their desk. They then record how many counters landed on or off the paper. You can individualize by choosing appropriate amounts for each student to work on.

Card Greeting

NCTM Content Standard:
Number & Operations

NCTM Process Standard:
Problem Solving

Specific math content or skill addressed:
Counting, number relationships

Component:
Greeting

Materials needed:
Number cards (0–10), enough for each student to have one

Preparing students for success:
Students need to have mastered the basics of friendly greetings.

Vocabulary:
Ordinal and cardinal numbers

How to do it:

■ Either before or at the start of the meeting, give each student a card.

■ All students stand in the circle.

■ The first student counts the number of people represented by the number on his playing card and greets the last person counted. (For instance, if she has a 3, she counts three and greets the third person she counted.) She then sits down in the spot of the person she greeted.

■ The person greeted then counts the number represented on his card, and so forth.

■ Students who are seated should not be counted but can be acknowledged with a friendly face.

■ As you near the end of the game (three people left standing), take student predictions about which person will be last to be greeted and why. Encourage students to use mathematical thinking as they make these predictions. For instance, if the greeting player has a 6, you could ask students to count six "in their heads" and see if they can figure out which of the two people will be greeted and who will be last.

VARIATION:

When students become adept at this greeting, have students work on their knowledge of directionality. Do this by having two different colors of cards— or if you use playing cards, just use the colors of the card suits. A student with a red card should count to the left, and a student with a black card should count to the right.

Class Detectives

How to do it:

- Post some version of the message to the right.

- Before the meeting, students write responses on scrap paper and hand them in to you.

- For the activity portion of the meeting, let students know that you are going to investigate their answers. Place the string down the middle of the circle to divide it in half. Label one half "yes" and one half "no."

- Read a question with the blank filled in. (For instance, if a student had written snakes, you would ask *"Do you like snakes?"*)

- Direct students who would answer "yes" to the question to go to the "yes" side and students who would answer "no" to the "no" side. Guide students on each side to count up their totals. Record those totals next to the word (for instance, "14 Y / 8 N").

- Repeat several times as time and energy allow.

- During the message portion of the meeting, read the words that you have not yet used. Let students know that you will investigate answers to those questions at math time.

- Ask students to look at the results so far and see what they noticed. Depending upon the answers, students might want to analyze their data further, investigate why people answered yes or no, and try to determine whether there are some common reasons for each answer. Students might also want to expand on their research by asking the same questions of other classes in the school.

EXTENSIONS DURING A LATER MATH LESSON:

- At math time, finish collecting data for the other questions if you did not do so at the meeting.

- Have students make graphs in various forms to show what they found.

NCTM Content Standard:
Data Analysis & Probability

NCTM Process Standard:
Communication, Connections

Specific math content or skill addressed:
Data analysis

Component:
Morning message, activity

Materials needed:
Scrap paper/pencils

Long piece of yarn to divide the circle in half

Message chart (for the morning message)

Preparing students for success:
The message portion of this activity should come after students have had considerable experience answering questions about themselves by interacting with the morning message, so this is a more appropriate activity for later in the year.

You will be using students' responses to the message during the activity portion of the meeting, so you may want to briefly look over the responses to make sure you can read them before the meeting begins.

Dear Curious Students,

I have asked you lots of questions to find out about you. I asked if you like pizza or hamburgers better. Then I asked you if you like to go to bed. Today YOU get to ask a question. Finish this question: "Do you like _____?"

We will ask your questions at the meeting.

A Clip and Save Meeting

NCTM Content Standard:

Number & Operations

NCTM Process Standard:

Connections, Communication, Problem Solving

Specific math content or skill addressed:

Money, counting

Component:

Greeting, sharing, activity or morning message (you could pick and choose any or all of the activities described)

Materials needed:

Grocery coupons of small value (10¢, 15¢, 20¢, or 25¢), enough total coupons for each student to have one

Real or play coins (nickels, dimes, quarters)

Message chart (for the morning message)

Preparing students for success:

Students should have prior experience or knowledge of what coupons are and how they work.

Students should have some prior experience counting coins.

Vocabulary:

Quarter, dime, nickel, coupon, save, how much, total, more than, less than

How to do it:

- Post some version of the message to the right.

- As students come to the meeting, give each of them a coupon. When all coupons have been passed out, pairs of students will have the same coupon.

- For the greeting:

  ✳ Call two students at a time to the middle to greet each other according to what product they have a coupon for. For instance: *"If you have a coupon for spaghetti sauce, come to the center of the circle and greet the other person who has that coupon."* Direct students to place coupons behind them once they have been greeted.

- For sharing:

  ✳ Do an around-the-circle share in which students share whether they would keep their coupons or trade with someone else in the circle and why. Model what this might look like. *"I would like to keep my coupon for cake mix because I love cake and want to save money!"* or *"I would like to trade my cake mix coupon for Noah's fruit coupon because I'm trying to cut back on unhealthy food."* (Be sure students understand that they will not actually trade coupons.)

- For the activity:

  ✳ Place coins in the center of the circle. Direct a few students at a time to come to the center and trade their coupons for the correct amount of coins. Model what this might look like with your own coupon.

  ✳ Once all students have traded, remove the coupons and extra coins from the center of the circle. Let the class know that you are all going to figure out now how much money you would have saved had you gone shopping for these items.

> Dear Smart Shoppers,
>
> Today we'll get coupons at our Morning Meeting. We will figure out how much money we would save if we really got to use them. Which of these would you rather buy, if you had a coupon?
>
> Peanut butter   Cheese

✳ Lead the class in counting all of the money everyone received for their coupons. For instance, you could make piles of all the quarters, dimes and nickels and find as many ways as you could to make dollars. Then, you would count the leftover change. Or, you might make piles of all the quarters, dimes and nickels and skip count by the appropriate amount.

■ For morning message:

✳ The class reads the message chorally. Have students say "cha-ching" for periods. Lead students to count how many chose peanut butter and how many cheese, which category had more and how many more, and what the total of those two categories is.

VARIATION:

Use a teacher-made spinner or die during the activity. Each portion of the spinner or side of the die could have different directions such as these:

■ It's double coupon day! You get twice the amount of money.

■ Your dog ate your coupon. Put your money back.

■ It's a regular coupon day. Just keep what you have.

On a given turn, students would roll the die and follow the directions.

EXTENSION DURING A LATER MATH LESSON:

Use even more coupons and have each student choose five at math time. Have them paste their coupons on the left side of a piece of paper. Then, on the right side, they should draw the correct amount and combination of coins needed to make their coupon value. As a challenge, on the back, they could figure out the total they saved.

Dice Greeting

NCTM Content Standard:

Number & Operations

NCTM Process Standard:

Problem Solving

Specific math content or skill addressed:

Counting, number relationships

Component:

Greeting

Materials needed:

One die

Preparing students for success:

Students need to have mastered the basics of friendly greetings.

Vocabulary:

Ordinal and cardinal numbers

How to do it:

■ All students stand in the circle.

■ The first student rolls the die and counts the number of people represented by the number rolled. She greets the last person counted. (For instance, if she rolls a four, she will count four people and greet the fourth person she counted.) She then sits down in the spot of the person she greeted.

■ The person greeted then rolls the die, counts the number represented on the die, and so forth.

■ Students who are seated should not be counted but can be acknowledged with a friendly face.

■ As you near the end of the game (three people left standing), take student predictions about what number(s) the person who is greeting will need to roll to greet one person or the other.

VARIATION:

When students become adept at this greeting, have students work on their understanding of odd/even and directionality. Do this by having students count in different directions depending upon whether they roll an odd or even number. A student who rolls an odd number should count to the left, and a student who rolls an even number should count to the right.

Favorites Graph

NCTM Content Standard:

Data Analysis & Probability

NCTM Process Standard:

Representation,
Communication

**Specific math content
or skill addressed:**

Graphs & diagrams,
data analysis

Component:

Morning message

Materials needed:

Message chart (for the
morning message)

**Preparing students
for success:**

Students need to have
some prior experience
with bar graphs.

Vocabulary:

Graph, most, least, equal

How to do it:

■ Include the following as a related task on your message:

On the graph below, color in one square to show your favorite fruit:

Apple	Orange	Grape	Peach	Other

Be sure students understand they should color starting from the bottom
squares. Each subsequent student will color in the next square up.

■ During the message portion of the meeting, guide students to understand
what the graph shows by asking some of these questions:

✳ *"What fruit do we like the most?"*

✳ *"What fruit do we like the least?"*

✳ *"Are any of the fruits equal?"*

VARIATIONS:

■ Repeat this activity with a different topic: favorite sport, book, pet, thing
to do after school, time of day, etc.

■ Vary the way the graph looks—for instance, by putting categories on the
left—so that students get practice with a wide variety of graphs.

EXTENSION DURING A LATER MATH LESSON:

Ask students to decide on their own research questions to ask classmates
and have them graph the results.

How Many to Ten?

NCTM Content Standard:

Number & Operations,
Algebra

NCTM Process Standard:

Problem Solving

**Specific math content
or skill addressed:**

Addition, counting

Component:

Activity

Materials needed:

Set of cards (0–10), with
four of each number

Pocket chart (optional)

**Preparing students
for success:**

Students should have some
prior experience with
addition and strategies
for addition.

Students should have
experience in partnering
up within the circle.

Vocabulary:

Number sentence, total,
how many more

How to do it:

- Shuffle the cards. On the pocket chart, display twenty to twenty-five of them face down. (If you do not have a pocket chart, this game will also work by displaying the cards in the middle of the circle. But, if you play it in this manner, be sure the numbers on the cards go both directions so all students can see them right side up.)

- Explain to students that the goal of this game is to have a set of cards that add up to ten.

- Randomly select one student. That student turns over two cards.

- Ask all of the students to think about how much those two numbers together would make and confer with a partner about this problem. Call on one set of partners to identify the total.

- If the numbers total ten, take that pair of cards out, place them together in a separate, visible location, and put two new cards in their place. If the sum of the numbers is greater than ten, turn the cards back over and call on another child to begin the next turn. If the sum of the numbers is less than ten, ask the child to turn over another card and have all the students think about the new total and begin the process anew.

- Continue playing for five to ten minutes by calling on several students to have a turn.

- As students take their turns, encourage them to think mathematically by asking questions like these:

  ❋ *"What number would _____ need to turn over to make ten? How do you know?"* (Ask this before a student has turned over his or her second card.)

  ❋ *"How did you figure out that three and five made eight?"*

  ❋ *"How could we show that five and four and one make ten in a number sentence?"*

EXTENSIONS DURING A LATER MATH LESSON:

- If you do not have time to finish the game at Morning Meeting, continue playing as a warm-up to begin your math lesson.

- Have students play the game with a partner at math time. Students could play by placing cards face down on the floor between them. First graders are very competitive, and competitive games are accordingly hard for them to do independently. However, if you have students play as pairs, you can give them a "team challenge" rather than having them play against each other: *"Let's see if the two of you together can get seven ways to make ten."*

How Much Space?

NCTM Content Standard:

Measurement

NCTM Process Standard:

Connections, Reasoning & Proof

Specific math content or skill addressed:

Measurement

Component:

Morning message

Materials needed:

Outline of your foot

Message chart (for the morning message)

Preparing students for success:

No special preparation is necessary.

Vocabulary:

Area, space, more, less

How to do it:

- Outline your foot, cut out the outline, and place it on the message where appropriate.

- Post some version of the message to the right.

- During the message portion of the meeting, ask students what they notice about their responses. Possible observations include:

  ✳ *"A lot of people found things that take up more space."*

  ✳ *"Three people found things that take up less space."*

  ✳ *"I am not sure some things are in the right place."*

- Choose several items and retrieve the actual object. Ask students to explain why they think it will take up more or less area or space than your foot. Ask students for ideas to figure out how much space each takes up. If needed, guide students with questions such as *"What if we filled up the space of each object with small things and then counted those small things? What type of thing might we use?"*

> Dear Students,
>
> We have measured lots of things on our bodies. Today I made a cut-out of my foot to see how much space it takes up. Find one thing that you think will take up more or less space than my foot, and write it below.
>
> More space   Less space

VARIATIONS:

- Use this same structure to explore other dimensions of measurement, including length, height, weight, perimeter, etc.

- The book *It Looked Like Spilt Milk* by Charles G. Shaw contains simple outline pictures, the areas of which are easy for students to measure. After reading the book to the students, post a message that asks students to predict which object in the book would take up the most space. Test the predictions at math time.

EXTENSIONS DURING A LATER MATH LESSON:

- Ask students to make an outline of whatever object they wrote on the message. Then, direct them to use cotton balls (or if a student has a better idea, use that) to measure the area. (Glue cotton balls side by side to fill the space.) At the end of the lesson, place the outlines in order from smallest area to largest area. Ask students what they notice or if any objects surprised them.

- Ask students to make an outline of their own feet and use cotton balls to measure the area.

Hundreds Chart Paths

NCTM Content Standard:

Number & Operations,
Algebra

NCTM Process Standard:

Reasoning & Proof

**Specific math content
or skill addressed:**

Place value, number
relationships

Component:

Activity

Materials needed:

One set of cards with digits
0–9, with four copies
of each number

Hundreds chart

Crayons or markers

Pocket chart (optional)

**Preparing students
for success:**

Students should be familiar
with the hundreds chart.

Students should have had
practice with the place value
concepts of tens and ones.

Vocabulary:

Tens place, ones place,
more, less, digits

How to do it:

■ Post a large version of the hundreds chart. Shuffle the number cards and place them face down in front of the chart.

■ Let the class know that the goal is to make a path that goes all the way from the top of the hundreds chart to the bottom or from one side to the other. The path has to have numbers that connect either side by side or top to bottom. Diagonals will not count as part of the path for this game.

■ Have a student turn over the top two cards and place them in the pocket chart. If necessary, the student should rearrange the cards to make the highest number possible. (For instance, if the student draws a 4 and a 6, she should switch the numbers to make 64). Have the student identify which digit is now in the tens place and which in the ones. Have another student color that number on the hundreds chart.

■ Another student may now choose a number that is ten less, ten more, one less, or one more than the number just colored (in our example, 54, 74, 63, or 65). Have a different student color that number as well. The second student's goal is to go in a direction that brings these colored squares closer to existing colored squares so that eventually colored squares connect to form a path.

■ Yet another student will draw and arrange two more cards, and another student will color that square. Another student will choose a number that is ten less, ten more, one less, or one more than the number just colored, another student will color that number, and so on.

■ Repeat these steps until the class has made a path going down or across the chart (or until time is up—in that case, continue the game at the beginning of math time).

EXTENSION DURING A LATER MATH LESSON:

Ask students to play this game with partners. The partners share a hundreds chart and take turns turning over cards, coloring the squares, and so forth. The game ends when, together, they make a path across or down the chart.

If I Were One Inch Tall

NCTM Content Standard:

Measurement

NCTM Process Standard:

Communication, Connections

Specific math content or skill addressed:

Measurement

Component:

Sharing, morning message

Materials needed:

Poem "One Inch Tall" by Shel Silverstein on a chart

Rulers

Message chart (for the morning message)

Preparing students for success:

Students should have prior experience with measuring in standard units.

Read the poem before the Morning Meeting.

It's helpful if, before doing this activity, students have identified "body measurements" such as *"My right thumb is one inch long."*

Vocabulary:

Measure, ruler, inch

How to do it:

- Post some version of the message to the right.

- During the sharing portion of the meeting, do an around-the-circle share in which each student completes the sentence, "If I were one inch tall, I would . . ." in a meaningful and unique way. After all students have shared, challenge them to reflect on what was shared by asking them various questions. For instance, you might ask *"Who remembers someone who shared what they would eat? Who remembers someone who shared something they would do outside?"*

- Read the message with "one inch voices." Read the objects students listed that were close to one inch tall. Test out a few by measuring them with a ruler.

> Dear Poem Lovers,
>
> We had so much fun reading Shel Silverstein's "One Inch Tall" yesterday. What makes his poems so interesting and funny?
>
> Use your rulers and find something in our classroom that is close to one inch tall. Write what you found in the space below:

VARIATIONS:

- Work on other measurements using the same structure: "If I were one centimeter tall," "If I were one meter tall," etc.

- Many other poems by Shel Silverstein (as well as other writers) lend themselves to Morning Meeting adaptations. For instance, if you read the poem "Band Aids," recite and act it out at Morning Meeting with actual bandages as props and then calculate the total. Similarly, act out the poem "Smart" using real or play money. The book *Number Parade: Number Poems from 0–100* also contains many math-based poems.

EXTENSION DURING A LATER MATH LESSON:

Give students a scavenger hunt challenge in which they have to find things that are one inch tall, one centimeter tall, four inches long, etc.

Magic Doubles

NCTM Content Standard:

Number & Operations,
Algebra

NCTM Process Standard:

None

**Specific math content
or skill addressed:**

Addition, identifying numbers

Component:

Activity

Materials needed:

Two dice

**Preparing students
for success:**

Students will need a partner
for this game, so assign those
quickly before or as the
activity starts.

This activity involves bodily
contact, so be sure to model
and practice gentle touching
before you start the round.

Students should have prior
practice with rolling dice
so that the dice stay
relatively close to the
person rolling them.

Vocabulary:

Addition facts, total or
sum, doubles

How to do it:

- Let students know that doubles are important for many reasons in math. In this game, everyone will roll the dice and calculate their totals. But, if someone rolls doubles, you will stand up and do a special chant and movement.

- Practice the chant first and then add the movements. Be sure to model gentle touching:

  Double, double bump, bump (bump hips twice with your partner)
  Double, double pump, pump (do a fist bump twice with your partner)
  Double, double jump, jump (jump up in the air twice)
  Double, double rump, rump (sit on your bottom and bounce twice)

- Hand two dice to the person who will start the game. That person rolls and calculates the total and states the roll and sum in a number sentence. For instance, if the roll resulted in a 3 and a 4, the student would say *"Three plus four makes seven"* or *"Three plus four equals seven."* Let other students know that their job is to try to figure out the total in their heads.

- The student passes the dice to the next person who follows the same steps. If a person rolls a double, students wait for that person to figure and announce the total and then, on your cue, they stand up to do the chant.

- Go around the circle so that everyone has a chance to roll at least once. Try to keep the pace quick without making students feel too rushed in terms of the calculation.

- Keep track of the number of doubles rolled. Say something like *"Wow! Nine out of twenty-two people rolled doubles. Do you think that is half of us or less than half? Why or why not?"* Take responses as time permits.

VARIATIONS:

- Once students have played this game several times, add a version of the following as a related task on your message: Today we will play Magic Doubles again. In the space below, predict how many doubles our class will roll today.

- During the message portion of the meeting, ask students to explain how they reached their predictions. Take note of whether students are using information from prior games or what other strategies they are using to make predictions.

■ Once students are adept at this game, it is also fun to have students switch places if they roll the same numbers as someone who came before them in the circle. Be sure to model and practice what this would look like and how to do it quickly, quietly, and safely.

EXTENSION DURING A LATER MATH LESSON:

Students can graph rolls of the dice on a graph that looks like the following:

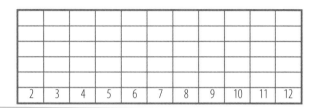

They could color the square for each sum and put a star in the center of it if they rolled a double to reach that sum.

Make a Shape

NCTM Content Standard:

Geometry

NCTM Process Standard:

Problem Solving, Reasoning, Communication

Specific math content or skill addressed:

Identifying shapes, part/whole relationships

Component:

Activity

Materials needed:

Shapes, one per student (pattern blocks or cut-out shapes work well for this activity)

Preparing students for success:

Students need to have some practice with naming shapes and understanding the properties of shapes.

Students should have played mix and mingle games in nonacademic ways before attempting this game. In particular, students need to know that when the chant stops they should find a nearby classmate rather than moving across the circle or searching for a particular friend.

Vocabulary:

Triangle, rectangle, square, trapezoid, parallelogram, quadrilateral, rhombus

How to do it:

- Teach students the following (or your own) chant:

  Triangle, rectangle, rhombus, square,
  Shapes around us everywhere,
  Two shapes together may make one
  Find a friend and start the fun.

- Give each student a shape. Examples are triangles, squares, rectangles, trapezoids, and rhombuses. You will need shapes that have at least one side equal to a side of the other shapes and can be put together to make new shapes.

- As they recite the chant, they walk around the circle, holding their shapes.

- When students get to the end of the chant ("*start the fun*"), they should find a nearby classmate.

- Each set of partners should sit down right where they are and find a way to combine their two shapes, but let them know that they may only join shapes on an equal side. Together they should decide what new shape they have found.

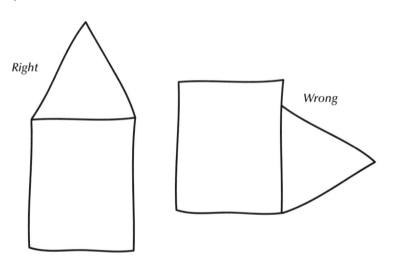

- Call on several pairs to share what they have found.

- Repeat several times.

- If you notice some pairs having difficulty deciding what their new shape is, show them how to quickly trace around it on a piece of scrap paper, as seeing only the outer edges may help them identify the shape.

VARIATION:

Give some students bigger shapes that could be composed of two smaller shapes. Instead of finding one partner, students should find two people whose shapes equal their own.

EXTENSION DURING A LATER MATH LESSON:

Give each student (or pairs of students) their own set of paper shapes and have them work with a partner to figure out what new shapes they can make by joining them at equal sides.

Measuring in Tens and Ones

NCTM Content Standard:

Measurement, Number & Operations

NCTM Process Standard:

Problem Solving, Communication, Connections

Specific math content or skill addressed:

Measurement, counting, sorting/grouping

Component:

Activity, morning message

Materials needed:

Unifix cubes

Message chart (for the morning message)

Preparing students for success:

Students should have previously worked with Unifix cubes.

Students should have experience counting by tens.

Vocabulary:

Distance, length, how long, how many, tens, ones

How to do it:

■ Post some version of the message to the right.

■ At activity time, ask students for some ideas of long things they could measure that are close to or within the meeting circle. (For instance, students could measure the distance across the Morning Meeting circle, how far it is from one student to another, how tall some people are, how tall the message chart is, how tall a cabinet or filing cabinet is, etc.) Choose one of these things to measure.

■ Model putting the trains of cubes together to measure the distance. Alternate colors of trains so that students can see distinct sets of ten. Use single Unifix cubes to measure the last bit of distance once a tens set would be too long.

■ Lead students in counting by tens and then ones the length of whatever you are measuring.

■ Repeat several times depending upon how much time you have. If appropriate, let students or sets of students put the trains together after your modeling.

■ During the message portion of the meeting, brainstorm and record at the bottom of the message chart other long things students could measure at a later time.

> Dear Measurers,
>
> Get ready to measure some LONGER objects in our room! Make a train of ten Unifix cubes of the same color. Place your train on our table. We'll use them at Morning Meeting to measure some BIG or LONG things.

VARIATION:

Play the game in reverse. Have a student roll a die. Another student puts together that many trains of tens. Have another student roll the die again, and another student selects that many single cubes. Count together the total number of cubes. Find something in the room that is close in length to the train you made.

EXTENSIONS DURING A LATER MATH LESSON:

■ If you have enough Unifix cubes, have students work with partners to measure in tens and ones some of the long things written on the message chart.

■ Students also enjoy this activity outside the classroom, so during rainy day recess or as time permits during math block, let them measure even longer distances (from one classroom to the next, etc.)

Number Grid Puzzle

NCTM Content Standard:

Number & Operations

NCTM Process Standard:

Communication,
Problem Solving

**Specific math content
or skill addressed:**

Number relationships,
counting, place value

Component:

Activity

Materials needed:

Hundreds grid cut into
enough pieces so that
each student in the class
can have one piece

**Preparing students
for success:**

Students should have played
mix and mingle games in
nonacademic ways before
attempting this game. In
particular, students need to
know that when the music
stops they should find a
nearby classmate rather
than moving across the
circle or searching for a
particular friend.

Students should also have a
strong understanding of
number patterns and the
hundreds grid.

Vocabulary:

Various numbers

How to do it:

- Give each student a piece of the grid.

- Instruct them that when the music begins, they should move about and find one other person whose piece would connect with their own. Once they find their person, they stop and wait.

- Stop the music. Make sure everyone has found someone else. Explore some ways people joined their pieces. For instance, students might say *"I had 9 and Katie had 10, so I knew we went together."* Or *"I had 13, and Sean had 23. We knew that the 13 was on top of the 23."*

- Play the music again. This time students should move as pairs and see if they can find another pair whose pieces match their own.

1	2	3	4	5	6	7	8	9	10
11	12	13	14	15	16	17	18	19	20
21	22	23	24	25	26	27	28	29	30
31	32	33	34	35	36	37	38	39	40
41	42	43	44	45	46	47	48	49	50
51	52	53	54	55	56	57	58	59	60
61	62	63	64	65	66	67	68	69	70
71	72	73	74	75	76	77	78	79	80
81	82	83	84	85	86	87	88	89	90
91	92	93	94	95	96	97	98	99	100

- Stop the music and make sure every pair has found another pair. Explore some ways people joined their pieces.

- At this point, direct pairs of students to sit together with the pair they matched.

- Work together as a class to finish completing the puzzle. For instance, you might say *"Tzipi, Josh, Caleb, and Lucy have a square with 68. Does anyone have a square that might join to 68?"*

- Celebrate completing the puzzle with brief dancing to the music.

EXTENSION DURING A LATER MATH LESSON:

Give students or pairs of students their own cut-up sets of hundreds grids to complete.

Pattern of the Day

NCTM Content Standard:

Algebra

NCTM Process Standard:

Connections

Specific math content or skill addressed:

Patterns

Component:

Activity

Materials needed:

None

Preparing students for success:

Students should have experience moving and taking turns in the circle.

Vocabulary:

Pattern

How to do it:

- Choose a "pattern of the day." You may want to begin with simple patterns like ABAB and then move on to more complex ones.

- First, make the pattern using students as parts of the pattern. For instance, if the pattern is ABAB, you might have one student stand, one sit, and so forth.

- Have students suggest movements to fit the pattern and choose two of those movements (for example, *stomp, clap, stomp, clap* or *snap, clap, snap, clap* or *forward, backward, forward, backward*).

- Practice the pattern by having it make its way around the circle. If the pattern is stomp, clap, the first student stomps, the second claps.

- Practice the pattern with all As making their movements, then all Bs making theirs, etc.

- Then, have students suggest some sounds to fit the pattern (such as *oom, pah, oom, pah* or *fa, la, fa, la*) and choose two.

- Practice the pattern with sound and movement by having it make its way around the circle.

- Practice the pattern with all As making their movements, then all Bs making theirs, etc.

VARIATION:

Incorporate some music content into this activity by working with the music teacher.

EXTENSION DURING A LATER MATH LESSON:

This activity also works as a warm-up at math time.

Quarters

NCTM Content Standard:

Number & Operations

NCTM Process Standard:

Problem Solving

**Specific math content
or skill addressed:**

Money, counting

Component:

Activity

Materials needed:

One die

Real or play coins (pennies,
nickels, dimes, quarters)

**Preparing students
for success:**

Students should have prior
experience counting coins.

Vocabulary:

Coin, trade, quarter,
dime, penny, nickel

How to do it:

■ Let students know that the goal of this game is to see how many quarters the class can get once everyone has a turn.

■ Place the coins in the center of the circle.

■ The first child rolls the die and takes the amount indicated in pennies. The child passes the coins and the die to the next person in the circle.

■ The second child rolls and gets the number of coins indicated. At this point, ask the class *"Can we trade any coins?"* If it is possible to make a swap (for instance, five pennies for a nickel), do so from the pile of coins in the center.

■ Continue playing in this manner until each child has had a turn.

■ At the end, see how many quarters the class has collected.

■ Discuss some of the students' ideas about what they could buy with the quarters.

VARIATIONS:

■ Make the game easier by playing for dimes or harder by playing for half dollars.

■ Let students play with two dice once they are able to count higher amounts.

EXTENSION DURING A LATER MATH LESSON:

Have students play this game with partners and see how many quarters they can get together within the time allotted.

Scoop 'Em Up

NCTM Content Standard:

Number & Operations, Data Analysis & Probability

NCTM Process Standard:

Problem Solving

Specific math content or skill addressed:

Counting, comparison

Component:

Morning message

Materials needed:

Small scoop(s)

Bowl of objects that fit in the scoop (popcorn kernels, raisins, dried beans)

Message chart (for the morning message)

Preparing students for success:

Students should have some experience counting large numbers of objects using strategies like grouping by tens.

Vocabulary:

Tens, ones, total, in all, smallest, largest, least, greatest

How to do it:

- Post some version of the message to the right.

- Notice how students are counting. Discuss their strategies with them.

- During the message portion of the meeting, prompt students to think about their results by asking some of these questions:

   ❊ *"Why do you think many of you got different numbers?"* Possible student responses include:

> Good morning, Counters!
>
> You have been counting lots and lots of objects at math time. Some of you put your objects in groups. Some of you counted twice to make sure you were right.
>
> Now we're going to count popcorn kernels! Fill up the scoop, count them, and write your number below:

   ✏ *"Because some people got the scoop fuller than other people."*

   ✏ *"Some of the kernels are different sizes, so if you got small ones, you would have more than people who had big ones."*

   ✏ *"Someone might have counted wrong."*

   ❊ *"If we were going to put these numbers from smallest to largest, which number would come first?"* (You may want to put all the numbers in order.)

   ❊ *"What are some strategies you used to count the objects?"* You may want to model a strategy a student suggests for other students.

   ❊ *"I wonder how much it would be if we combined all of our numbers together?"* This question is clearly very difficult for first graders but may give you some insight into their mathematical thinking.

VARIATION:

Rather than having students individually count, just have them take out one scoop of the material and place it in a large container. During the message portion of the meeting, lead the whole class in counting the material, modeling grouping by tens.

■ Pop some of the popcorn, or bring some prepopped popcorn. Count out a certain number of unpopped kernels and compare it with the same number of popped kernels, or show concepts of volume by putting the unpopped kernels in an appropriate size container and the popped corn in another.

■ Have partners take out one scoop each of the material and count it separately. Then, have them count their two scoops together.

Seconds, Minutes, Hours

NCTM Content Standard:

Measurement

NCTM Process Standard:

Connections, Reasoning & Proof

Specific math content or skill addressed:

Time, counting, comparison

Component:

Activity

Materials needed:

Stopwatch, timer, or watch or clock with a second hand

Preparing students for success:

Students should have some familiarity with basics of time, such as there being sixty seconds in a minute and sixty minutes in an hour.

Be careful as you go through the steps of this activity to minimize competition. Keep the focus on understanding how long ten seconds is, not who can do the most in ten seconds.

Vocabulary:

Minute, second, time, how long, how many, strategy, prediction

How to do it:

■ Let students know that this morning they will have a chance to explore time. First, work with ten seconds. Have students close their eyes and put their heads down. Tell them when you are starting to measure the time and then have them put their heads up when they think ten seconds have elapsed. Ask students *"What strategies did you use to try to mark the seconds or decide when to raise your head?"* Possible responses include:

❋ *"I just counted to ten kind of slowly."*

❋ *"My dad taught me to count like this: one Mississippi, two Mississippi . . ."*

❋ *"I tried to think of the hand of a clock in my head and count with the hand."*

■ Repeat once more.

■ Then, ask students how high they think they can go counting by twos in ten seconds. Take a few predictions, let students know when to start, and then time students to find out.

■ Repeat with how many times they can clap in ten seconds. Try to do the counting together as you time so that it does not become competitive and you have an accurate count.

■ Repeat with how many times they can jump in ten seconds. Again, try to do this together if possible.

■ Now ask students *"If you can jump _____ times in ten seconds, how many times do you think you can jump in a minute, or sixty seconds?"* Ask a few students *"How did you come up with that prediction?"*

■ Time the class for a minute, and see how many times they can jump. Compare it with the number for ten seconds.

■ Repeat with clapping.

■ End by having students close their eyes, put their heads down, and raise their heads when they think a minute has gone by.

VARIATION:

Students build their sense of how long a given span of time is by repetition. Other things to try include:

■ Standing on one foot for ten seconds or a minute

■ Writing/drawing for ten seconds or a minute

- Bouncing a ball for ten seconds or a minute

- Singing a familiar tune (like "Row, row, row your boat" or "Happy Birthday") for ten seconds or a minute

EXTENSION DURING A LATER MATH LESSON:

If you have timers or a class clock with a second hand, have students work with partners to predict and then count how many times they can do certain things in ten seconds or sixty seconds.

Shape Hunt

NCTM Content Standard:
Geometry

NCTM Process Standard:
Connections, Communication

**Specific math content
or skill addressed:**
Identifying shapes

Component:
Sharing, morning message

Materials needed:
Message chart (for the
morning message)

**Preparing students
for success:**
Students should be familiar
with basic shapes, their
names, and their properties.

Vocabulary:
Shape names, properties
of shapes (terms such as
sides, corners, lines, etc.)

How to do it:

■ Post some version of the message below.

> Dear Shape Hunters,
>
> Yesterday we looked for shapes in our school.
>
>
> We found squares, triangles, rectangles, circles, pentagons, and lots more.
>
> Today we'll look for shapes in our classroom. Be looking around our room and see if you find a shape. We'll share what we find at Morning Meeting.

■ During the sharing component, go around the circle and have students share the shapes they found and where they found them. Alert other students to be listening closely to what people share.

■ Ask students questions about what they heard others share. For instance, you could ask *"Who remembers someone who found a square?"*

■ During the message portion of the meeting, prompt students to think more deeply about the shapes they found by asking questions like the following:

❋ *"How did you know it was a hexagon (square, rectangle, etc.)?"*

❋ *"No one found any rhombuses. I wonder if we look around now if we can see any."*

❋ *"Are there any shapes some people found that could fit inside shapes that other people found?"*

VARIATIONS:

■ Students share about shapes they found in their homes.

■ Do this sharing over several days and let students share more extensively about their shapes and take questions or comments. For instance, students might say why they chose the shape, discuss shapes they rejected first, etc. Students might talk about how hard it was to find the shape, why they like rectangles (squares, etc.), and whether the shape was the same/different from shapes the student found on other shape hunts.

■ Show students famous paintings (in books, calendars, at a museum, etc.) and ask them to share about shapes they see in those.

Start with Ten

NCTM Process Standard:

Problem Solving

**Specific math content
or skill addressed:**

Addition, subtraction

Component:

Activity

Materials needed:

Colored tiles or Unifix cubes

One +/– die

Regular die

**Preparing students
for success:**

Students should have a
beginning understanding of
addition and subtraction.

Vocabulary:

Add, subtract

How to do it:

■ Place ten colored tiles or Unifix cubes in the center of the circle. Keep some more tiles or cubes in a box that travels with the die from student to student.

■ Let students know that you will be adding to and subtracting from the tiles or cubes in the center. The goal of this game is to make it all the way around the circle without removing all of the tiles or cubes.

■ On a given student's turn, she rolls both the +/– die and the regular die and adds or subtracts a number of tiles or cubes according to what she rolled. (If you do not have a +/– die, you can make one by writing on a blank cube with a marker or putting labels on a regular die and writing on the labels. The die should have three sides with the + symbol and three sides with a – symbol.)

■ If, on a given turn, the roll results in a number less than zero, that round ends. Add ten more to the circle and begin again.

EXTENSION DURING A LATER MATH LESSON:

Students can play this as a partner game. The partners take turns rolling the dice and adding or subtracting tiles or cubes according to the roll. If they run out of tiles or cubes, they start over again.

This Group, That Group

NCTM Content Standard:

Algebra

NCTM Process Standard:

Reasoning & Proof,
Communication

**Specific math content
or skill addressed:**

Sorting/grouping

Component:

Activity

Materials needed:

Hula-hoops, large circles of
yarn, or some other objects
big enough to hold a small
group of students (optional)

**Preparing students
for success:**

No special preparation
is necessary.

Vocabulary:

Groups, sorting, similar,
in common, alike

How to do it:

- Secretly choose two categories of students. For instance, you might begin by thinking of students who are wearing white shirts and students who are not.

- Place two Hula-hoops (or large circles of yarn, etc.) in the center of the circle. Without revealing why you are putting them there, ask a few students representative of each category to stand in one of the circles. (If you do not have Hula-hoops or yarn, this activity also works if you have one group stand on your left and one on your right.) You do not need to put every child who would fit in the category in the circle—a few students will be sufficient.

- Ask students to study who is in each group and try to figure out why you put some students in one category and some in the other. You could also ask *"Who else might go in each Hula-hoop?"*

- If students cannot figure out your reasoning, encourage them by asking questions like *"What is similar about these students? "What do they all have in common?"* or *"How are they all alike?"*

VARIATIONS:

- Begin with fairly obvious categories based on concrete, visible attributes, but over time (after doing this activity several times) move to more abstract attributes. Here are a few categories to consider:

  ✳ Clothing colors or characteristics (words on shirt, no words on shirt, etc.)

  ✳ Shoe colors or types

  ✳ Hair styles (long vs. short, ponytail vs. no ponytail, etc.)

  ✳ Socks vs. no socks

  ✳ Jewelry vs. no jewelry

  ✳ Students who sit at the same tables

  ✳ Students who all have the same kind of pets (dog people in one circle, cat people in another)

  ✳ Students who all share a similar interest (group that plays soccer, group that plays basketball)

- Play this game with objects that can be sorted into two categories, like beads, stuffed animals, or shapes.

EXTENSION DURING A LATER MATH LESSON:

Have students independently sort groups of objects in a similar way.

Tiles in a Bag

NCTM Content Standard:

Number & Operations

NCTM Process Standard:

Reasoning & Proof,
Communication

**Specific math content
or skill addressed:**

Addition

Component:

Morning message

Materials needed:

Brown bag containing
colored tiles (from set
that has four colors)

Message chart (for the
morning message)

**Preparing students
for success:**

Students will need to be
familiar with and have
used the colored tiles
prior to this activity.

How to do it:

■ Include some version of the following related task on your message:

I have put 12 tiles in this bag. How many of each color could be in the bag?

Have the students write their guesses on the message chart. Responses could include *"4 red, 4 blue, and 4 green,"* or *"6 red and 6 green"* or *"3 red, 2 blue, 4 green, and 3 yellow."* You might want to do an example with abbreviations so that students do not have to write as much—for instance, 3R, 1Y, 4B, 4G.

■ During the message portion of the meeting, look over students' responses. Ask the students what they notice about them. Possible responses might include:

✳ *"We came up with twenty-three different ideas!"*

✳ *"Lots of people think there are six red ones in the bag."*

✳ *"Lots of people used all four colors."*

■ Ask *"Do you think you have enough information to be sure that your answer is correct? If not, what would help?"*

■ Let students know that at math time, you will give them more clues to figure out which tiles are in the bag.

EXTENSION DURING A LATER MATH LESSON:

Display students' responses from the morning. Give pairs of students a small set of tiles to use as you give them clues so that they can figure out what is in the bag. Begin giving students clues. For instance, if the bag contains six red tiles, three green tiles, and three yellow tiles, you might say *"The bag has no blue tiles."* Your next clue might be *"It has the same number of green and yellow tiles."* Students would take a few minutes to figure out new possible combinations. Continue to narrow the possibilities.

A Trail Mix Recipe

NCTM Content Standard:

Measurement, Number
& Operations

NCTM Process Standard:

Connections, Problem Solving

**Specific math content
or skill addressed:**

Measurement, fractions

Component:

Morning message

Materials needed:

1 cup, $\frac{1}{2}$ cup, and $\frac{1}{4}$ cup
measuring cups

Message chart (for the
morning message)

**Preparing students
for success:**

Students should have
some basic familiarity with
measuring cups and what
they are used for.

Vocabulary:

$\frac{1}{4}$, $\frac{1}{2}$, cup, measure

How to do it:

- Post some version of the following message:

Dear Chefs,

Today we will measure as we make up a recipe for trail mix. We will start the recipe at Morning Meeting and finish it at math time.

Choose one item to add to our trail mix. Write whether you want to add $\frac{1}{4}$ cup or $\frac{1}{2}$ cup to our recipe. Be sure to look at what your classmates have already written!

Corn Cereal   Marshmallows   Raisins   Pretzels   Oat Cereal

Also, have the two sizes of measuring cups available for students to see.

- During the message portion of the meeting, ask students what they notice about what their classmates have written. See if anyone wants to change his or her addition to the recipe.

- Take one category (like corn cereal) and say something like the following: *"Four people have written $\frac{1}{4}$ cup for the corn cereal. I wonder how much that is."* Take ideas from students. Then, measure out the smaller amounts into the full cup and/or $\frac{1}{2}$ cup as appropriate to get a total measurement for the corn cereal. Finish by saying something like *"So four $\frac{1}{4}$ cups make one whole cup."*

VARIATION:

Try the same structure with other recipes. For instance, have the students as a group invent (and try making) their own fruit salads, juice combinations to make a unique type of juice, or ice cream toppings.

EXTENSION DURING A LATER MATH LESSON:

Finish combining smaller measurements into bigger ones. Talk students through what you are doing as you do this. Use the final recipe to make the trail mix and divide it equally among students. Have them evaluate the recipe and graph the results. Questions could include whether there was enough for everyone, whether it tasted good, and whether it should have had more or less of certain ingredients.

Two Is King

NCTM Content Standard:

Number & Operations,
Algebra

NCTM Process Standard:

Problem Solving

**Specific math content
or skill addressed:**

Number relationships,
patterns

Component:

Activity

Materials needed:

Number cards (0–12), with
four of each number

Pocket chart (optional)

**Preparing students
for success:**

Students should have
experience figuring out the
difference between two
numbers. This might be
difficult for first graders, so
you may want to post a
hundreds chart and practice
finding numbers that are
"two apart" before attempting
this activity.

Vocabulary:

Difference, how far away,
how far apart

How to do it:

■ Let students know that in this game two is the magic number. Every time the class finds a pair of numbers that are two apart, they can keep that pair. The goal is to see how many pairs they can make before the game is over.

■ Turn over the top two cards from the deck. Display them in the pocket chart or the center of the circle.

■ Ask students to calculate whether these numbers are two away from each other (or you could ask whether the difference between them is two, or whether they are two apart). For instance, if the cards showing were 3 and 5, their difference would be two. Call on one or two students to share whether they believe the difference is or is not two and how they figured that out. If the difference is two, the class can keep those two cards, and you can turn over two new cards.

■ If the difference is not two, turn over one more card and see if the difference between it and one of the other cards is two. If it is, make a pair to keep. If not, turn over another card until you have a pair that is two apart.

■ Continue playing for five to ten minutes. At the end, see how many pairs you have made.

VARIATION:

Depending upon their achievement levels, have students look for other differences while playing this game, including numbers that are one, three, or five apart.

EXTENSION DURING A LATER MATH LESSON:

Have students play this game with partners and see how many pairs of numbers they can find that are two apart.

Are You a Rectangle?

NCTM Content Standard:

Measurement, Geometry

NCTM Process Standard:

Reasoning & Proof

Specific math content or skill addressed:

Measurement, identifying shapes

Component:

Morning message

Materials needed:

Posted directions

String/yarn (two colors)

Scissors

Message chart (for the morning message)

Preparing students for success:

Students should have some experience working with partners.

Following these directions might take awhile, so this activity works best if students are in the classroom well before Morning Meeting.

Students should have some experience using and cutting string to measure objects.

Vocabulary:

Measure, length, height, span, equal, longer, shorter, square, rectangle

How to do it:

- Post some version of the message to the right.

- On the board, post these directions:

Work with a partner to do these things:

Have your partner cut a piece of blue yarn to measure your height.

Hold your arms straight out to your sides and have your partner cut a piece of red yarn to measure your arm span.

Compare the two strings to see which is longer or whether they are the same.

Save your strings for math time by placing them in a safe place in your desk.

Dear Measurers,

Yesterday we worked with partners to measure around our heads and waists. Wasn't it surprising that the distance around your waist is longer than your arm? This morning we are going to use string to measure our height and arm span. Follow the directions on the board and then write your name in the appropriate space below:

| My height is longer than my arm span. | My height is shorter than my arm span. | My height and arm span are the same. |

- During the message portion of the meeting, let students know that the measurement they took will show if their body is a square or rectangle. Choose one student from each column to demonstrate this. Cut two strings to equal each student's height and two strings to equal their arm span. Use the strings to build a square or rectangle on the floor around the student.

- Relabel the categories on the message as "tall rectangle," "wide rectangle," or "square."

EXTENSIONS DURING A LATER MATH LESSON:

- Have students measure their strings in standard units and record their heights and arm spans.

- Have students select pictures of characters from books or famous works of art and figure out how to measure their height and arm span to determine whether the person is a tall rectangle, wide rectangle, or square.

Bouncing Balls

NCTM Content Standard:
Data Analysis & Probability

NCTM Process Standard:
Connections, Representation

Specific math content or skill addressed:
Graphs & diagrams, data analysis

Component:
Morning message

Materials needed:
Bouncy ball

Message chart (for the morning message)

Preparing students for success:
Students need to be fairly adept at reading the message and following directions.

Students should have some prior experience with line graphs and other types of graphs.

The first time you do this activity, it may help to prepare students the day before, near dismissal time. Draft the next day's message and the board directions early and show them to students. Also, model how to read and follow them.

Vocabulary:
Least, greatest, most, graph, about how many

How to do it:

■ Post some version of the message to the right.

■ On the board, post these directions:

———————

1. Hold the ball straight out from your waist.
2. Drop it.
3. Count how many times it bounces before stopping.
4. Record your results on our graph.

———————

Dear Scientists,

We have been talking about how important it is to be careful and have good information for science. One way scientists do this is to use several tests of the same object or occurrence.

This morning we are going to practice these skills with bouncy balls.

To help us get ready, follow the directions on the board and then:

—Place a sticker on our line graph to show how many bounces you had.

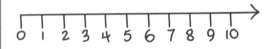

■ A completed graph might look like this:

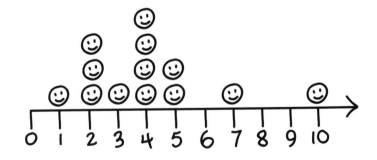

76

- During the morning message part of the meeting, reflect on the data the students have gathered. Here are some questions you might ask:

  ✴ *"What do you notice about our results?"* Possible student responses include:

    ✏ *"Lots of people had four bounces."*

    ✏ *"Somebody had ten bounces!"*

    ✏ *"One person's ball only bounced once."*

    ✏ *"The ball might have gotten tired at the end."*

  ✴ *"What was the least number of bounces? What was the greatest? So, our numbers range from _____ to _____."*

  ✴ *"What number falls in the middle of our range?"*

  ✴ *"What number of bounces happened most frequently?"*

  ✴ *"Look at the graph and tell me what could we say if someone asked us, 'About how many bounces can you get from dropping this ball?'"*

VARIATIONS:

- This structure can be used many times with a variety of balls. Save the graphs and compare the balls with each other.

- Have students drop two balls from the same height and record which one bounces the highest.

Broken Calculator

NCTM Content Standard:
Number & Operations, Algebra

NCTM Process Standard:
Problem Solving, Reasoning & Proof

Specific math content or skill addressed:
Addition, subtraction, algebra

Component:
Morning message

Materials needed:
Calculators

Message chart (for the morning message)

Preparing students for success:
At math time, teach students how to play Broken Calculator. In this game, students pretend that certain keys, designated by you, are broken. They have to make a target number appear in the calculator display without using those broken keys. For instance, a teacher might say that the 2 and 4 keys were broken and ask students to make 24. To solve this problem, one student might write the equation $10 + 10 + 1 + 3$. Another might write $30 - 6$.

Make sure students understand and feel comfortable with this game before using it in your message.

Vocabulary:
Addition, subtraction, equation, calculator

How to do it:

■ At the end of your morning message, include a related task like the following:

Pretend that the 2 and the + key on your calculator are broken. How can you make the number 20 appear on the display of your calculator? Write one equation below.

Be sure to include space for one equation per student.

■ When you come to the message component of the meeting, have students reflect in some way on their equations. You might ask one of the following questions:

✳ *"Was it hard to have the + key broken? Why or why not?"*

✳ *"What do you notice about our equations?"* Possible responses might include:

✎ *"Lots of people used 1 a lot."*

✎ *"Almost everyone used subtraction."*

✎ *"They are all different."*

✎ *"Two people had really complicated ones!"*

✳ *"How many different operations did people use?"*

✳ *"Which equations would work if we did them in the opposite direction? Which would not?"*

VARIATIONS:

■ If you want students to focus on a particular operation, make all the operation keys except that one "broken." Also, if you notice students are often using the $1 + 1 + 1$ strategy and want to challenge them to think more deeply, make the 1 key broken.

■ Instead of telling students which keys are broken, have them try to figure that out. For instance, you might write as your related task:

I am trying to display 36 on my calculator. Here are a few equations that will work: $10 + 10 + 10 + 4 + 2$; $40 - 4$; 9×4; $5 + 5 + 5 + 5 + 5 + 5 + 5 + 1$. What keys might be broken?

EXTENSION DURING A LATER MATH LESSON:

Challenge students to come up with several new equations that were not included in their responses to the message. Or add an additional "broken key" and see which equations would still work.

Grade Level 2

Card Combination Game

NCTM Content Standard:

Number & Operations, Algebra

NCTM Process Standard:

Reasoning & Proof, Problem Solving

Specific math content or skill addressed:

Identifying numbers, addition, odd & even, multiplication

Component:

Activity

Materials needed:

Set of cards with two numbers each. See the example for a classroom set of 20.

Preparing students for success:

Students should have had some direct teaching and practice about any math concepts used for the categories.

Vocabulary:

Sum, odd, even, product, less than, more than

How to do it:

- Each student receives one card.
- Explain to students that you will call out a category and that they will try to find one or more people whose card(s) fit in that category. When they find that person or those people, they will stop and wait for your signal.
- Call out a category for students to use to find a match. Examples:
  - ✻ Someone who has one of the same numbers as you
  - ✻ Someone who has the same even number as you
  - ✻ Someone who has the same odd number as you
  - ✻ Someone whose two numbers have the same total, or sum, as yours
  - ✻ Someone who has a number that is one less than one of yours
  - ✻ Someone who has a number that is one more than one of yours
  - ✻ Someone whose product is the same as yours

8 0	7 0	4 5	6 3	9 2
6 5	3 10	9 4	6 6	10 2
0 6	2 4	6 2	3 4	5 2
10 1	3 8	6 4	8 2	4 4

- Use the signal to gain students' attention and help students who have not yet found partners.
- Go through several categories.

Catch the Bug

NCTM Content Standard:

Number & Operations,
Algebra

NCTM Process Standard:

Problem Solving,
Reasoning & Proof

**Specific math content
or skill addressed:**

Addition, subtraction, algebra

Component:

Activity

Materials needed:

Chart paper

**Preparing students
for success:**

Students will understand how
to play the game better if
they have played the game
with words or phrases.

Students should have some
basic number sense and
familiarity with addition
and subtraction.

Vocabulary:

Add, subtract, number
sentence, equation

How to do it:

- Prepare a secret number sentence.

- Represent that number sentence on the chart with blanks. For instance, if your secret number sentence is $10 + 10 + 10 + 3 + 3 = 36$, you will write on the chart __ __ + __ __ + __ __ + __ + __ = __ __. Also draw a basic spiderweb.

- Select students randomly or call upon volunteers to guess a number from zero to nine. If the number is contained in your number sentence, fill in all of the places the selected number would go. If the number is not contained in your number sentence, add a body part to a bug who may be caught in the spider's web. (Note: A bug has three main body parts and six legs.)

- Let students know that as soon as they think they can guess the number sentence, they may try, but a missed guess will add a body part to the bug.

- You might guide some of this guessing by encouraging students to think about the numbers that are already up there and what might be in the blanks to make the number sentence or equation true. You might ask *"Look at the numbers we already have in the ones place. What number do we need in our last ones blank to make the equation work?"*

Give It Time

NCTM Content Standard:

Measurement, Data
Analysis & Probability

NCTM Process Standard:

Connections, Representation

**Specific math content
or skill addressed:**

Prediction, graphs & diagrams

Component:

Morning message

Materials needed:

Nail

Container to hold water

Message chart (for the
morning message)

**Preparing students
for success:**

Students will need to have
some experience with
recording information on
a bar graph.

Students should be aware
of how scientists predict
and observe, and understand
that estimates are scientific
predictions and not attempts
to "win!"

Vocabulary:

Graph, how long, temporal
language (days, weeks, etc.)

How to do it:

■ Include the following related task on your message:

Today we will begin an experiment. We will place a nail in the container of water. On the graph below, predict when we will see a change in the nail by coloring in one square:

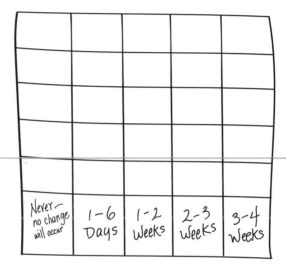

■ During the message portion of the meeting, reflect on the predictions by asking some of these questions:

❋ *"What do you notice about our graph?"*

❋ *"If you are in one of these columns* (indicating all the columns except the "never"), *what change do you think we will see?"*

❋ *"How did you decide which square to color in?"*

■ Save the message (or at least the graph) and compare the results with students' predictions once you see a change.

VARIATIONS:

■ Use something besides a nail. Many combinations of substances might produce change: a piece of bread in a moistened bag, a penny in lemon juice, a piece of celery or apple buried in moist dirt. However, you may need to change the choices for predicted ranges of time depending upon which of these substances you choose.

■ Instead of having students mark their predictions on the graph, have them mark them on a large version of a calendar. Record change/no change on the calendar each day.

Graphing Pockets

NCTM Content Standard:

Data Analysis & Probability

NCTM Process Standard:

Connections,
Communication,
Representation

**Specific math content
or skill addressed:**

Graphs & diagrams,
data analysis

Component:

Morning message

Materials needed:

Unifix cubes in a bowl
or container

Message chart (for the
morning message)

**Preparing students
for success:**

Students should have some
prior experience with line
graphs and other types
of graphs.

Vocabulary:

Graph, least, greatest,
range, estimate

How to do it:

■ Post some version of
the message to the
right.

■ Have these directions
on the board:

_____

1. Put a Unifix cube in each
pocket of your clothing.

2. Take the cubes out and
make a train with them.

3. Count your total and put
your train in our bowl.

_____

Dear Mathematicians,

Today at math time we are going to
figure out how many pockets we are
all wearing today!

Follow the directions on the board
and then place a sticker on our line
graph to show how many pockets
you have:

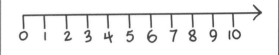

■ A completed graph might look like this:

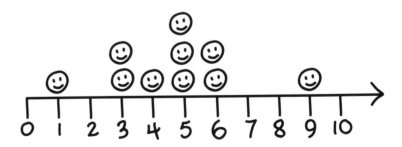

■ During the morning message part of the meeting, reflect on the data the
students have gathered. Here are some questions you might ask:

❋ *"What is the least number of pockets someone has? What is the
greatest? So, our numbers range from ____ to ____."*

❋ *"What number falls in the middle of our range?"*

❋ *"What number of pockets do most people have?"*

82

✳ *"Is there a different way we could graph these numbers?"*

✳ *"Looking at the graph, can you estimate what the total number of pockets for our class will be?"*

VARIATION:

Have students count and graph:

- Buttons or zippers on their clothing

- Alphabet letters or numbers on their clothing

- Colors on their clothing

EXTENSIONS DURING A LATER MATH LESSON:

- At math time, guide the class in counting up the total number of pockets. Combine all of their individual Unifix cube trains. Then, break them down into groups of tens and remaining ones.

- Have students graph the information in bar graph form.

- Have students write about what the graph tells them. For instance, a student might write *"Five people in our class have ten pockets on their clothing. Four people have no pockets. Most people have two, three, or four pockets."*

Guess My Number

How to do it:

- Tell the class *"I'm thinking of a number between zero and one hundred. Guess this number. I'll answer yes-and-no questions only."*

- The students shrink the range by asking questions like *"Is the number even?" "Is the number less than fifty?" "Is the number a multiple of five?"*

- Once the students narrow the range down to a small amount, around five, they guess the number.

VARIATIONS:

- Increase the range once the students understand how the game works.

- One student leaves the room and the class decides on a secret number that has some connection to the class or classroom (examples might be the number of eyes of everyone in the classroom, the number of chairs, or the number of bookshelves). Students work with a partner to think of clues that will help the guesser figure out the secret number. The clues should help the guesser narrow down the choices. After the student who is outside returns to the middle of the circle, she calls on pairs to give their clues and tries to figure out the number and what that number represents in the classroom. (Note: This variation might feel risky to some students. So wait to play this game until the class has a comfortable, safe sense of community.)

Guess *Your* Number

NCTM Content Standard:

Number & Operations

NCTM Process Standard:

Communication,
Reasoning & Proof

**Specific math content
or skill addressed:**

Attribution, mathematical
description, estimation

Component:

Activity

Materials needed:

Index cards (one for each
child) with a different
number on each card

Tape

**Preparing students
for success:**

Some prior experience
playing Guess My Number
(page 84) as a group will help.

Students should have
practice with mingling.

Vocabulary:

Even, odd, greater than,
less than, range, digit

How to do it:

■ Tape a card to each student's back. The cards should be prepared ahead of time with a different number on each card.

■ Students mingle, looking at one another's numbers when they meet and asking each other questions to determine the number on their backs (asking directly for the number is not allowed).

Questions might include:

❋ *"Is it even?"*

❋ *"Is it odd?"*

❋ *"Is it greater than _____?"*

❋ *"Is it less than _____?"*

❋ *"Is it between ____ and _____?"*

❋ *"Is it in the range ___ – ___?"*

❋ *"Is it a two-digit number?"*

■ To keep it active, say that you may ask only one question per classmate, then you must move on and ask somebody else.

■ Tell students that they must ask three questions before guessing actual numbers, even if they think they know it.

VARIATIONS:

■ Play with one student in the middle of the circle. This student has a number on her back and asks the group questions. Students raise their hands to answer, or everyone answers aloud. This is a good way to introduce the activity and to come up with some good questions to ask so that everyone can be successful when everyone is playing at the same time.

■ Choose numbers to support students' current number work. Fractions or decimals could also work.

EXTENSION DURING A LATER MATH LESSON:

Ask students what questions worked well and make a list. Hang this list on the board when you play again.

Guess *Your* Shape

NCTM Content Standard:

Geometry

NCTM Process Standard:

Communication,
Representation

**Specific math content
or skill addressed:**

Identifying shapes,
mathematical description,
estimation

Component:

Activity

Materials needed:

Index cards (one for each
child) with a different
shape on each card

Tape

**Preparing students
for success:**

Some prior experience
playing Guess My Number
(page 84) as a group will help.

Students should have
practice with mingling.

Vocabulary:

Various polygons, specifically
named curved shapes such as
ovals and circles, specifically
named quadrilaterals

How to do it:

- Tape a card to each student's back. The cards should be prepared ahead of time with a different shape on each card.

- Students mingle, looking at one another's shapes when they meet and asking each other questions to determine the shape on their backs (asking directly for the shape is not allowed).

Questions might include:

❊ *"Is it a polygon?"*

❊ *"Does it have a curve in it?"*

❊ *"Can this shape be found in the room?"*

❊ *"How many corners does it have?"*

❊ *"How many sides does it have?"*

- To keep it active, say that you may ask only one question per classmate, then you must move on and ask somebody else.

- Tell students that they must ask three questions before guessing actual shapes, even if they think they know it.

VARIATIONS:

- Play with one student in the middle of the circle. This student has a shape on her back and asks the group questions. Students raise their hands to answer, or everyone answers aloud. This is a good way to introduce the activity and to come up with some good questions to ask so that everyone can be successful when everyone is playing at the same time.

- Choose shapes to support students' current work with geometry. For example, you might start off with a simple range of shapes early in the year and complicate the selection as the students experience more geometry during the year.

EXTENSION DURING A LATER MATH LESSON:

Ask students what questions worked well and make a list. Hang this list on the board when you play again.

Human Polygons

NCTM Content Standard:

Geometry

NCTM Process Standard:

Communication

**Specific math content
or skill addressed:**

Identifying shapes

Component:

Activity

Materials needed:

Chart paper (optional)

**Preparing students
for success:**

Students should be able to
recognize shapes according
to various attributes such
as length of sides, square
or right angles, and other
types of angles.

Vocabulary:

Sides, lines, angles,
corners, length

How to do it:

■ Explain to students that today the class is going to practice their understanding of shapes by making some shapes with their bodies. Hopefully,
everyone will have a chance to help make a shape, but when it is not
their turn to be part of the shape, they will need to be careful observers
and assistants.

■ Use the number four to guide students through the first example. Ask
four students to lie on the floor and make a shape. Each student must lie
straight, like a line segment. Two students can join together to be one line
as long as they fit within the circle, or each child could be a separate
line. The end of each line must touch the end of another line. If necessary,
help the first set of students arrange themselves into a shape.

■ Ask the observing students to stand up and look at the shape. Guide the
observing students through looking at and analyzing the shape that results.
Sample questions: *"What would you call that shape? What do you notice
about its angles (corners)?"*

■ (Optional) Record a quick drawn version of the shape and its name on
the chart paper.

■ Send the four students back to their places in the circle.

■ Sticking with the number four, ask another group of students to come
to the circle and see if they can make a different shape.

■ Repeat the process for the number four several times.

■ Choose another number and repeat the entire process.

■ Sample round:

Four students come to the middle of the circle and form a square.

Teacher: *"What shape did they make?"*

Student 1: *"A square."*

Teacher: *"What can you tell me about the corners (angles) on this
square?"*

Student 2: *"They are all square corners"* (or right angles, depending
upon the vocabulary you have taught the students).

CONTINUED ▶

Human Polygons

Teacher: *"If I replaced one of the students in the square, would it still be a square? Talk to your elbow partner and see what you think."* (After appropriate amount of thinking/talking time) *"So, what do you think?"*

Student 3: *"We think you couldn't make a square with you in it."*

Teacher: *"Why not?"*

Student 4: *"Because you are taller than everyone else, and to be a square, all the sides have to be the same size."*

Teacher: *"I can see you are really thinking about what it takes to be a square. Let's see if four more people can make a different shape."*

■ Tip: Keep the discussion moving quickly so that students retain their interest and all have a chance to make a shape. Remember that the activity portion of the meeting should only last about ten minutes.

EXTENSION DURING A LATER MATH LESSON:

You can use this activity as a math warm-up lesson. Give each student a set of straight line objects (Cuisenaire rods, different length pieces of yarn), some the same length and some different. Give students a number and ask them to make a shape with that many of their lines. Record possibilities.

It Could Be a . . .

NCTM Content Standard:

Geometry

NCTM Process Standard:

Communication, Connections

**Specific math content
or skill addressed:**

Identifying shapes

Component:

Sharing

Materials needed:

Two to four two-dimensional
or three-dimensional shapes

Chart

**Preparing students
for success:**

Students should have some
prior experience with shapes.

Students should have some
prior experience with sharing
and speaking in front of their
classmates. (You may want
to give students time before
the meeting to think of ideas
or take notes about what
they want to say.)

Vocabulary:

Shape names, lines, angles

How to do it:

- Before beginning Morning Meeting, write a sentence frame on the chart:
  "I know this is a _____(shape), but it could be a _____."

- Place two to four two- or three-dimensional shapes in the center of the circle. (Choose shapes that fit what you have been studying in prior geometry lessons.)

- Let students know that today they will be imagining what these shapes could be.

- Choose one and model what sharing will look like. Example: *"I know this is a cylinder, but it could be my new tube of lipstick."*

- Give students time to think of their sentences.

- Alert the group to be listening, as you will play a challenge game at the conclusion of sharing.

- Go around the circle and allow each student to share.

- For each shape, see how many different things students can remember that people suggested and list those on a chart. Encourage students to keep thinking about the possibilities.

EXTENSIONS DURING A LATER MATH LESSON:

- Return to the brainstormed list during math time and see if students have thought of any other items to add.

- Find several items that students named and bring those into class. Compare them to your geometric examples and discuss how they are similar or different, emphasizing distinctive properties of the shapes. For instance, you might hold up the tube of lipstick and a cylinder shape and ask *"How are these two shapes similar?"* Possible responses include:

  ❋ *"They both have a circle on the top and bottom."*

  ❋ *"They both are curved all the way around."*

  ❋ *"They are both tubes."*

Magic 20

How to do it:

NCTM Content Standard:

Number & Operations, Algebra

NCTM Process Standard:

Problem Solving, Communication

Specific math content or skill addressed:

Addition, algebra

Component:

Activity

Materials needed:

Number cards (0–10), with four of each number

Pocket chart (optional)

Preparing students for success:

Students should have some prior experience with addition and finding the missing addend.

Vocabulary:

Add, sum, how much more, difference

- Shuffle the cards and place the stack in the center of the circle or near the pocket chart.

- Explain to students that the goal of this game is to get as close to twenty as possible with three cards.

- Randomly select one student. That student takes three cards from the top of the pile and displays them in the center of the circle or on the pocket chart.

- Ask all of the students to think about how much these three numbers together would make and confer with a partner about this problem. Call on one set of partners to identify the total.

- If the numbers total twenty, the class stands and calls out "Bingo" (or some other designated word).

- If the numbers do not total twenty, ask students to figure out how far the total is from twenty by conferring again with their partners. Ask a few sets of partners to explain how they figured out the difference.

- Continue playing for five to ten minutes by calling on several students to have a turn.

VARIATIONS:

- Keep track of how far from twenty the numbers are each time and figure out a total for that Morning Meeting. Keep a record of the "score" for that day and compare the next time you play.

- List on a chart or board the number sentences for each problem on each turn.

EXTENSIONS DURING A LATER MATH LESSON:

- Have students play this as a math warm-up game.

- Have students play this as a partner game. In the partner version, they put the stack of cards between them. On a given turn, each partner draws three cards, totals them, and sees who is closer to twenty.

Make the Number

NCTM Content Standard:

Number & Operations

NCTM Process Standard:

Problem Solving

**Specific math content
or skill addressed:**

Place value

Component:

Activity

Materials needed:

Large numeral cards (0–9),
enough for each student
to have one

**Preparing students
for success:**

Students should already
have some familiarity
with place value.

Model how to move
about safely throughout
the center of the circle.

Model how to stop, look
at you, and await further
instruction when the
music stops.

Students should have played
other games that require
mingling and/or moving to
music. (Maitre D' and People
to People are two examples.
See *The Morning Meeting
Book* and *Energizers! 88 Quick
Movement Activities That
Refresh and Refocus, K–6* for
directions for these and
similar games.)

Vocabulary:

Hundreds, tens, ones

How to do it:

- Give each student a large numeral card.

- Play some music. While the music is playing, students move around the circle. When the music stops, each student finds a partner. The partners make the biggest number they can by combining the numbers on their cards. For instance, if one student had a 2 and his partner had a 3, they would arrange their cards to make 32.

- When everyone has found a partner, each pair quickly reads their numbers.

- Ask a few pairs which number is in the tens place and which is in the ones place.

- Challenge pairs to put themselves in order from smallest to largest silently.

- Repeat the process several times.

VARIATIONS:

- Have students try to make the smallest number possible instead of the largest.

- Vary the level of difficulty by adding more partners (three for a hundreds place, four for a thousands place) as students are ready.

- Have students round the number they make to the nearest ten if you have taught rounding.

EXTENSION DURING A LATER MATH LESSON:

As a math activity, have students use smaller numeral cards to make numbers and then work to place those numbers in order from smallest to largest. For instance, give each student a small set of cards. They should turn over two (or three) at a time and write down the largest number they can make with those. (If a student draws a 2 and 6, she combines them to make 62). Once the student has used up all the cards and written down all the numbers, she then puts the numbers she has made in order from least to greatest.

Math Book Sharing

NCTM Content Standard:

Varies depending upon
book chosen

NCTM Process Standard:

Communication,
Connections, and various
others, depending upon
book chosen

**Specific math content
or skill addressed:**

Varies depending upon
book chosen

Component:

Sharing

Materials needed:

Children's book

Chart paper (optional)

**Preparing students
for success:**

On the day before the
Morning Meeting during
which you will be sharing, read
students a children's book
involving math concepts
appropriate to what you are
studying. (See book ideas in
the variation section.)

Prompt students to be
thinking about a new idea
based on the book. (See
ideas for innovations in
the variation section.)

Vocabulary:

The language will vary
depending upon the
book you choose.

How to do it:

■ Remind students about the book you read the prior day. Let them know that each of them will have a chance when sharing today to share a new idea based on the book. For instance, if the book you read was *Two of Everything* by Lily Toy Hong, students can share what they would want to put in the magic pot, how many they would put in, and how many they would expect to get out. Model what the sharing should sound like. You might say *"I would put my twelve baseball cards in the magic pot, and I would expect to get out twenty-four baseball cards."* You might also want to use a sentence frame.

■ Give students some time to think about their responses.

■ Have students turn to partners and practice sharing their responses.

■ Then go around the circle and let each student share.

■ As students share, you may want to chart responses either for future use as a class book or to show the mathematical representation of what was shared (*e.g.,* 12 + 12 = 24).

■ You may also want to give students a listening task while others share. For instance, you might say *"Be listening to what your classmates share, as we are going to be putting some things into categories afterwards and seeing what we can remember."* Afterwards, ask questions like *"Who can remember someone who shared something about an animal they would put in the magic pot?"* *"Who can remember someone who shared something about a food they would put in the magic pot?"*

VARIATIONS:

■ Some other books that would work well for this sharing include:

✳ *12 Ways to Get to 11* by Eve Merriam—have students share their own personal ways to get to 11 (for instance: *"I could get to eleven by adding my three sisters plus my two parents plus my six pets."*)

✳ *Each Orange Had 8 Slices* by Paul Giganti—have students share what they saw on the way to grandma's (for instance: *"On my way to Grandma's, I saw three cats. Each cat had two eyes, eight whiskers, and four paws."*) In math class later, students can write and solve problems based on each other's ideas.

✳ *Alexander, Who Used to Be Rich Last Sunday* by Judith Viorst—have students share the dumbest thing they ever wasted money on and how much they wasted. Keep track and, together or as a challenge at math time, have students figure out (1) how much total money they wasted and (2) something they, as a class, could buy if they had that money back.

■ For longer books, have only a few students share on the topic per day so that they can take questions or comments.

EXTENSION DURING A LATER MATH LESSON:

Record students' statements and have each student write, illustrate, and represent mathematically a page about the statement. Then compile those into a class book.

Measure Yourself

NCTM Content Standard:
Measurement

NCTM Process Standard:
Problem Solving,
Connections

Specific math content or skill addressed:
Measurement

Component:
Morning message

Materials needed:
Rulers or tape measures

Message chart (for the morning message)

Preparing students for success:
Students will need to have some prior practice measuring with standard units.

Vocabulary:
Measure, inches, centimeters, distance, most, least, longest, shortest

How to do it:

■ On the message, include the following as the related task:

Use the tape measure or ruler to measure the distance in centimeters between your wrist and the inside of your elbow. Record your result with your name in the space below.

■ During the message component of the meeting, review students' answers to the message by asking some of these questions:

❋ "What do you notice about your responses?" Possible student responses:

✏ "They are all pretty close to ____ (a certain number)."

✏ "Maria's is the longest!"

✏ "Mine is the shortest."

✏ "A lot of people are really close to my number."

✏ "Some people might not have measured correctly."

❋ "Can you think of any objects in our classroom that might be about the same as the distance from your wrist to your elbow?"

❋ "If we were to measure the distance from your wrist to your elbow in inches, would that be more or less than the measurement in centimeters?"

VARIATION:

Have students measure the length of their feet, circumference of their heads, length of their smile, length of their longest strand of hair, and distance between their knee and ankle.

EXTENSION DURING A LATER MATH LESSON:

Have students work in pairs to trace outlines of themselves and measure various distances on their outlines.

2

Money for Nothin'

NCTM Content Standard:

Number & Operations

NCTM Process Standard:

Problem Solving

**Specific math content
or skill addressed:**

Counting, money

Component:

Activity

Materials needed:

One die

Variety of real coins
(if possible)

Chart

**Preparing students
for success:**

Students should have prior
experience counting
up coins.

During this activity, each
student will receive a coin.
Consider what students
should do with their coins or
where they should place
them while you are going
around the circle (behind
them, placed in circle twelve
inches in front of them, etc.)

Vocabulary:

Penny, nickel, dime,
quarter, total

How to do it:

- Post a chart similar to the one at the right.

- The goal might just be to see how much money students can make, or you can make this game more interesting and challenging by giving the students a target amount. For instance, the target could be $4.00. The challenge would be to see how close to the target the class could get without going over. Students who have a free choice can ask classmates for advice about what coins to choose.

1 =	Penny
2 =	Nickel
3 =	Quarter
4 =	Dime
5 =	Nickel
6 =	Free Choice

- Go around the circle and let each student roll the die. For each roll, the student selects the appropriate coin.

- Ask students to rearrange themselves so that they are sitting in the circle according to their coins (pennies together, nickels together, etc.)

- Lead students to figure out the total by asking them ways they could combine themselves to make dollars and then figure out leftover change. Call on a student to record the total.

- If you are playing for a specific target ($4.00), figure out how far the total is from the target—for instance, by using the strategies of counting up or counting down.

VARIATIONS:

- Have students try to line themselves up in the order of the dates on their coins.

- Let students play this game individually by rolling a predetermined number of rolls, obtaining the coins, and calculating their totals.

- Have students play this game with a partner. On a given turn, each partner rolls the die and gets the appropriate coin. At the end of the game, each partner figures out his or her total.

Name Patterns

How to do it:

- In this activity, you will be doing a rhythmic pattern based on the consonants and vowels in people's names. Consonants should have one movement (for instance, clapping) and vowels should have another (for instance, snapping the fingers or slapping the thighs).

- Let students know that you will secretly choose one of their names and turn it into a clapping pattern. Tell them which movement will represent consonants and which vowels. Reference a place in the classroom (chart or word wall) where they can find each other's names.

- Clap and snap for the first person you selected. For instance, if the child's name is Allison, the pattern will be *snap, clap, clap, snap, clap, snap, clap*. Stop and show the same pattern with Unifix cubes (for instance, blue, yellow, yellow, blue, yellow, blue, yellow). This visual representation will help some students keep up with the pattern.

- Have students join in with you and repeat the pattern several times.

- Stop and see if anyone can figure out whose name it is. If more than one student has the same pattern, accept as correct all responses from those who guess one of these students.

- Repeat for another student's name.

EXTENSION DURING A LATER MATH LESSON:

At math time, ask students to build a Unifix train representing the consonant-vowel pattern in their name. Have them search in the dictionary, books, etc., for other words that follow the same pattern.

NCTM Content Standard:

Algebra

NCTM Process Standard:

Problem Solving,
Connections

**Specific math content
or skill addressed:**

Patterns

Component:

Activity

Materials needed:

Display of students' names

Unifix cubes

**Preparing students
for success:**

Students need to know and
be familiar with the spelling
of each other's names.

Students need to have
a good understanding of
vowels and consonants.

Vocabulary:

Pattern

Name Values

NCTM Content Standard:

Number & Operations

NCTM Process Standard:

Problem Solving

**Specific math content
or skill addressed:**

Addition

Component:

Morning message

Materials needed:

Chart of letter values

Scrap paper and pencils

Message chart (for the
morning message)

**Preparing students
for success:**

Students should have some
experience with adding
strings of numbers and
know some strategies
for doing so.

Students might also benefit
if they do a comparable
activity before the meeting.

Vocabulary:

Value, least, most, equal,
add, total

How to do it:

■ Prepare a chart like the one at the right that gives values to letters of the alphabet.

■ On your morning message, include the following related task:

Use the letter value chart to figure out how many points you would get for each letter of your first name. Then, add those points together. Write your name and your total in the space below.

■ During the message portion of the meeting, reflect with students on the results by asking some of these questions:

❋ *"Whose name has the least number of points?"*

❋ *"Whose name has the most points? So, the range of our names goes from ___ to ___."*

❋ *"Whose names are equal in value?"*

❋ *"If we were going to add up all of our names together, how many points do you think we would have? How could we find out?"*

A = 1	N = 1
B = 3	O = 1
C = 3	P = 3
D = 2	Q = 10
E = 1	R = 1
F = 4	S = 1
G = 2	T = 1
H = 4	U = 1
I = 1	V = 4
J = 8	W = 4
K = 5	X = 8
L = 1	Y = 4
M = 3	Z = 10

Example: CAT 3 + 1 + 1 = 5

VARIATIONS:

■ Repeat for middle names, last names, etc.

■ In the message ask students to choose a word (from the word wall, dictionary, a unit of study, etc.) and calculate the total for that word.

■ Use different letter values: five points for consonants, ten for vowels, or a coin value for each letter, etc.

EXTENSIONS DURING A LATER MATH LESSON:

■ Figure out the whole class total.

■ Ask students *"If you could change one letter in your name, which letter would you change and why? What would your new name and value be?"* Let students share their responses.

■ As a class or individually, have students graph the results from the message.

Roll a Big One

NCTM Content Standard:

Number & Operations

NCTM Process Standard:

Problem Solving, Reasoning & Proof, Communication

Specific math content or skill addressed:

Place value

Component:

Activity

Materials needed:

Chart paper

One die

Preparing students for success:

Students should have experience with place value.

Let students know that in this game everyone will think together about the best move to make, but for each turn only one student will get to choose the actual move. Model and practice how to react neutrally even if you would make a different choice.

Vocabulary:

Ones place, tens place, larger than, bigger than, more than, less than, least, greatest

How to do it:

■ On a blank piece of chart paper, draw the following shapes large enough so that you will be able to draw numbers inside each shape that students can see:

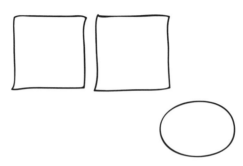

■ Explain to students that they will take turns rolling the die. Their challenge will be to make as big a number as they can by placing the number rolled in either the ones box or the tens box or the oval "trash can." Once a student decides on where to put a number, it can't be moved again.

■ Ask or draw a name for a student to roll a die.

■ Ask or draw a name for another student to place the number. Ask the student to explain why she made that decision.

■ Repeat the process until both squares and the trash can are filled.

■ Ask everyone to reflect on what number they made, whether they have made the biggest number possible, and how they know.

■ Here is how a sample round and conversation might look:

TURN ONE

Teacher: *"Why do you want to place the four in the ones place?"*

Student: *"Well, four is pretty big, so I don't want to throw it away. But I hope someone rolls a 5 or 6 for the first box, so I don't want to fill that up."*

TURN TWO

Teacher: *"Why do you want to throw the three away?"*

Student: *"I think that we could still get a bigger number for the first box, and three is not that big."*

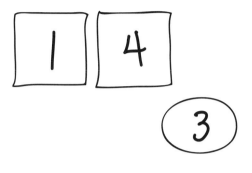

Teacher (to whole class): *"What is our number?"*

Student 1: *"Fourteen."*

Teacher: *"Is it the biggest number we could make?"*

Students (in unison): *"No!"*

Teacher: *"How do you know?"*

Student 2: *"We could make thirty-four. That is bigger."*

Student 3: *"Also, forty-one is bigger."*

Teacher: *"Is forty-one as big a number we could make?"*

Student 4: *"No, we could make forty-three."*

Teacher: *"Is that the largest number we could make?"*

Students (after thinking): *"Yes."*

VARIATION:

As the year progresses and students' understanding of place value grows, add the hundreds and then the thousands places.

EXTENSIONS DURING A LATER MATH LESSON:

- This game also serves as a great warm-up game for math time. Ask students to make their own recording sheet or use a recording sheet you made that looks like the chart above. You can roll the die and on each turn, students can make their own decisions about where to place the numbers. List all the numbers students make.

- Play this game as a partner game. Give each set of partners one die and have them take turns rolling it. They can play several rounds and see who has the higher number on each round.

Six Rolls to 100

NCTM Content Standard:

Number & Operations

NCTM Process Standard:

Problem Solving, Reasoning & Proof

**Specific math content
or skill addressed:**

Place value, addition, mental math

Component:

Activity

Materials needed:

One die

Base ten blocks

Score chart (see sample)

**Preparing students
for success:**

Students should have some experience
with using base ten blocks.

Let students know that in this game
everyone will think together about
the best move to make, but for each
turn only one student will get to choose
the actual move. Model and practice
how to react neutrally even if you
would make a different choice.

During the course of the game, many
students will get to roll the die, but it is
possible not every student will have a
turn. Be prepared to discuss ways that
students can participate (doing the
math in their heads, cheering on their
teammates, etc.) even if they do not
get a chance to roll.

Vocabulary:

Add, total, how close, how far,
more than, less than

How to do it:

■ Explain that the basic goal of this game is for the class to have a score as close to 100 as it can by the end of the game without going over 100. The class will have six turns to get to 100. On each turn, someone will roll the die, and the class will think about whether to choose that many rods (tens) or that many pieces (ones). Once the class makes a decision on a turn, that is it. It is not possible to go back later and change the decision on a turn.

■ Begin by choosing one child (in some random way) to roll the die.

	Rods	Pieces	Total so far
1			
2			
3			
4			
5			
6			

■ Ask students to confer with a person next to them about whether the class should get rods (tens) or pieces (ones) for the amount rolled.

■ Use the quiet signal to regain students' attention. Call on one student to make the decision. Remind students of how to care for that classmate.

■ Record the decision on the chart and have another child gather that many rods or pieces.

■ Ask the class *"What is our total so far?"* Record the total so far on the chart.

■ Repeat these steps until the class has taken six turns. As students confer with partners, remind them to be sure their decision doesn't put the class total above 100.

■ A finished game chart might look like the example to the right.

■ After the round is finished, ask students to reflect on the game. You might ask *"How far from 100 were we?" "Do you wish we had made any decisions differently?" "Do you think we were lucky or unlucky in this game?"*

	Rods	Pieces	Total so far
1	4		40
2		2	42
3		6	48
4	3		78
5		5	83
6		2	85

■ You might want to keep game charts for future reference.

VARIATIONS:

■ After students become more adept with and develop a better understanding of place value, begin to move them to a less concrete level. Use dimes and pennies instead of rods and pieces. Move to playing the game with no manipulatives and discuss mental math strategies students could use to figure out the total so far.

■ Later in the year, as students become even more proficient, play the game in reverse. Begin at 100 and see how close you can get to zero without going under by subtracting each time. When and if you play this way, remember to return to using concrete manipulatives.

EXTENSIONS DURING A LATER MATH LESSON:

■ This game also serves as a great warm-up game for math time. Students can make their own recording sheet or use one you made that looks like the chart above. Roll the die, and on each turn, let students make their own decisions about where to place the numbers. One caution is that students often need to make some visible mark in the column they did not choose so that they don't inadvertently record in that spot on the next turn. For example, if the roll is two, and the child chooses two rods, she can put an asterisk in the pieces column.

■ It is also possible to play this game as a partner game. Each set of partners has one die and takes turns rolling it. At the end, they determine who is closest to 100 without going over.

Skip Greeting with Cards

NCTM Content Standard:

Number & Operations

NCTM Process Standard:

Problem Solving

Specific math content or skill addressed:

Addition

Component:

Greeting

Materials needed:

Number cards, enough for each student to have one

Preparing students for success:

Students should already have practiced and gained skill with friendly greetings.

Students should have had some practice with basic addition facts.

Vocabulary:

Least, greatest, add, sum, equal

How to do it:

- Give each student a number card.

- All students stand in the circle.

- The first student counts according to the number on her card and greets the last person counted. For instance, if the child has a 2, she counts two and greets the second person she counted.

- The two students add their two numbers to figure out their sum.

- The student who was counting and greeting then sits down in the spot of the person she greeted.

- The person greeted then counts the number represented on his card and so forth.

- Once students are seated, they should not be counted but can be acknowledged with a friendly face.

- Alert the other students to be listening for which pair has the greatest sum, least sum, or equal sums. At the end of the greeting, call on several students to share this information.

Spinners

NCTM Content Standard:
Data Analysis & Probability

NCTM Process Standard:
Reasoning & Proof,
Communication

**Specific math content
or skill addressed:**
Data analysis

Component:
Morning message

Materials needed:
A variety of spinners, both
"fair" and "unfair"

Message chart (for the
morning message)

Vocabulary:
Graph, fair, more, less

How to do it:

■ Set out a spinner for students to use. "Fair" spinners land on different colors with equal frequency—for example, half the time on red, half the time on blue. "Unfair" spinners land on some colors more often than others—for example, half the time on red, one-fourth of the time on blue, one-fourth of the time on yellow.

■ On the message, include the following as the related task:

Spin the spinner in front of the message chart. Record your result by coloring in a space on the graph below.

■ During the message portion of the meeting, ask students to reflect on the results of their tests:

✳ *"What do you notice about our graph?"* (The following example assumes the use of an unfair spinner.) Possible student responses:

☞ *"There's a lot more blue than red and yellow."*

☞ *"The spinner landed on blue thirteen times, on red six times, and on yellow seven times."*

☞ *"If you add red and yellow up, they are the same as blue."*

✳ *"Do you think the spinner is fair or not fair?"* Possible student responses:

☞ *"I think it is not fair because the numbers should be equal."*

☞ *"I think it is not fair because half of it is blue, and that is bigger than yellow or red, so it might land on blue more."*

☞ *"I think it is fair because it has three colors, and it can land on any of the colors."*

VARIATION:

The value of this activity increases the more you do it, so try it with a variety of spinners.

Venn Diagrams

NCTM Content Standard:

Data Analysis

NCTM Process Standard:

Reasoning & Proof,
Representation

**Specific math content
or skill addressed:**

Graphs & diagrams,
data analysis

Component:

Morning message

Materials needed:

Message chart (for the
morning message)

**Preparing students
for success:**

No special preparation
is necessary.

Vocabulary:

Venn diagram

How to do it:

■ Prepare a message with a Venn diagram as the related task. Here is an example:

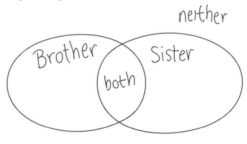

Dear Second Grade Scholars,

Today we will read another book by Patricia Polacco called *My Rotten Redheaded Older Brother*. As usual, Patricia Polacco based her story on her own life. The story is about a girl who is always competing with her older brother. Do you have any siblings?

■ On the day before you are going to use a Venn diagram for the first time, show it to the students. Explain where they would place their names depending upon which type of sibling(s) they have (or if they have any siblings at all).

■ Be close by the message during the next morning as students enter to reinforce your teaching from the day before.

■ During the message portion of the meeting, discuss the results with the students. You might use an open-ended question like *"What do you notice about who in our class has siblings?"* Possible student answers might include:

✽ *"More people have brothers than sisters."*

✽ *"Two people have no siblings."*

✽ *"Four people have both brothers and sisters."*

Or, you could be more narrow and ask questions like *"How many students in our class have brothers?" "How many have sisters?" "How many have both?" "How many are only children?"* In either instance, you could also add each category to see how many total students are present for the day.

■ Once introduced, use this organizational tool in your message repeatedly. Use questions that would fit the above Venn diagram structure, such as *"Which pet would you like to have, a dog or a cat?" "Which book that we read did you like better,* Knuffle Bunny *or* Don't Let the Pigeon Drive the Bus?"

■ You could also ask different Venn diagram format questions like these:

"Which do you live in?"

"Which kind of snack should we have for our math game celebration?"

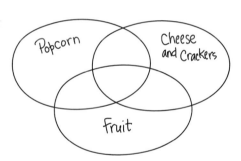

EXTENSIONS DURING A LATER MATH LESSON:

■ Have students sort various shapes using Venn diagrams. For instance, ask students to sort triangles according to whether they have corners (angles) that are smaller or larger than square corners (angles).

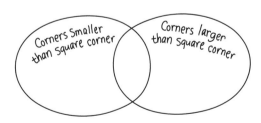

CONTINUED ▶

Venn Diagrams

- Have students sort numbers or equations using Venn diagrams. For instance, give students or pairs of students a set of number cards and ask students to organize them according to numbers you reach counting by twos and numbers you reach counting by threes. Afterwards, ask what they noticed.

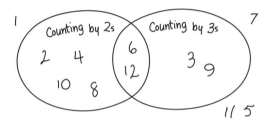

- Have students sort objects according to various measurements. For instance, ask students to sort objects that have a length greater than a certain amount and a width greater than a certain amount.

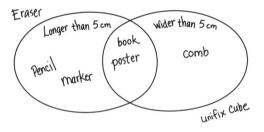

What Number Am I?

NCTM Content Standard:

Algebra

NCTM Process Standard:

Reasoning & Proof,
Problem Solving

**Specific math content
or skill addressed:**

Addition, algebra

Component:

Activity

Materials needed:

Enough index cards for each
child to have one: about ⅔ of
the cards should have a variety
of numbers from 0 to 5 and
about ⅓ should be blank

**Preparing students
for success:**

Model how to move
about safely throughout
the center of the circle.

Model how to stop, look
at you, and await further
instruction when the
music stops.

Students should have played
mix and mingle games in
nonacademic ways before
attempting this game.

Vocabulary:

Sum, addend, represent

How to do it:

■ Give each student a card.

■ Play music and let students dance or mill about to music.

■ When the music stops, have students form groups of three. One of the three should have a blank card. (If the class does not divide equally into groups of three, the last group could consist of two or four students.)

■ Provide the students with a sum. Begin with lower numbers like eleven or twelve. As students become more mathematically adept, increase the sums.

■ Tell students that they need to add their numbers to equal the target sum, so they need to figure out what number the blank card represents.

■ Go around and let groups share their combinations.

■ Have players within each group switch cards.

■ Repeat the process several times and encourage students to form new groups of three (following the rule of two numbers and one blank) each time the music stops.

■ Reflect on the process with students by asking *"What strategies did you use to figure out what number the blank represented?"* Students might say some of these things:

❋ *"We added two of the numbers and then counted up to the target."*

❋ *"We added two of the numbers and then subtracted the total from the target."*

❋ *"We went over to the hundreds chart and used it to add our two numbers and to count to the target number."*

EXTENSIONS DURING A LATER MATH LESSON:

■ Use some of math time to have students discuss and compare the strategies they used to figure out missing numbers.

■ Once students are comfortable with this activity, write x, y, or other letters on the cards to represent the missing number.

■ Once you reach the stage when students are using letters instead of blanks, save the last set of combinations and have students write their equations at math time: $5 + 4 + x = 12$.

Base Ten Block Building

NCTM Content Standard:

Number & Operations

NCTM Process Standard:

Representation

**Specific math content
or skill addressed:**

Identifying numbers, addition,
subtraction, multiplication,
sorting/grouping

Component:

Activity

Materials needed:

Multiple sets of base
ten blocks

Multiple pairs of dice

**Preparing students
for success:**

Students should have
experience with base ten
blocks, place value, using
two dice at a time, and
working with addition
and multiplication.

Students should be able
to move safely in a
crowded area.

Vocabulary:

Addends, difference, factors,
products, equals, sum,
equation, estimate, regroup

How to do it:

■ Post sets of base ten blocks at various points outside of the circle. The students will retrieve the blocks they need from these piles. Make sure they are in places students can walk to safely, because many students will be accessing these piles as the game progresses.

■ Pair up the students and give each pair two dice. You should also set a time limit for this activity.

■ One partner rolls the dice. Each die becomes an addend, and the two partners agree on the sum. The nonrolling partner goes to a pile of base ten blocks, retrieves the amount equal to the sum, and places them in the center of the circle. All students will put the blocks they retrieve in one pile in the center of the circle.

■ The partner who retrieved the blocks rolls the dice and the two again agree upon the sum. The student who didn't roll the dice this time retrieves the amount equal to the sum and then brings them to the pile in the circle.

■ The pair regroups the pile of blocks in the center of the circle by going back to one of the designated piles to acquire the necessary blocks for the regrouping. For example, if the students arrive at the center pile with a 10 and two 1s and the pile is composed of four 10s and nine 1s, they must regroup the amount and replace the pile with six 10s and one 1.

■ The pile in the middle of the circle will grow—students should assist one another as the regrouping becomes more difficult.

■ After the time limit is reached, the students estimate the total amount in the middle. Split up the pile and give students smaller piles to count. Record the counted amounts and again have the students estimate the total sum. Then (or later during math time) have the students compute the amount using calculators or pencil and paper.

VARIATIONS:

■ Alter the dice to produce higher amounts once the students have mastered the typical amounts on the dice.

■ Doing this game with multiplication can increase the challenge and is an easy adjustment once the students understand the process.

■ Begin with an amount of base ten blocks in the center of the circle and have the students take away the amount they have rolled while continuously regrouping the pile in the center.

Beach Ball Tossing

NCTM Content Standard:
Number & Operations

NCTM Process Standard:
Communication,
Problem Solving

**Specific math content
or skill addressed:**
Identifying numbers, addition,
subtraction, multiplication,
sorting/grouping

Component:
Activity

Materials needed:
A beach ball with numbers
written on or taped to
each section

**Preparing students
for success:**
Students should know how
to appropriately toss objects
to one another in the circle.

Before beginning the activity,
remind the students to toss
the ball to as many other
students as possible and
to be aware of who hasn't
received the beach ball yet.

Vocabulary:
Depending on the operation,
addends, difference, factors,
products, equals, sum, and
equation as appropriate

How to do it:

- Begin by modeling how to toss and catch the beach ball. When you catch the ball, model how one hand will land on one section of the ball and another hand will land on another section. Explain that this is important because each section has a different number.

- Gently toss the beach ball to a student.

- The student who receives the ball computes the sum, product, or difference of the numbers she is touching with the student to her left. For example, when the ball is caught, the student might have one hand on 10 and the other hand on 3. If addition is being practiced, the student turns to the child to her left and together they would determine the sum. Then they announce the entire math sentence: *"Ten plus three equals thirteen."* If multiplication is being practiced, the students would announce *"Ten times three equals thirty."*

VARIATIONS:

- Vary the numbers to include fractions or decimals when the students are ready for more advanced math concepts.

- During a fraction unit, the students can determine whether the sum of the fractions is more than or less than a whole. For example, if one fraction is $\frac{2}{3}$ and the other fraction is $\frac{1}{2}$, the students would announce *"$\frac{2}{3}$ plus $\frac{1}{2}$ is more than a whole."* Having manipulatives handy may be a good idea for visual reinforcement.

Body Math

NCTM Content Standard:
Measurement, Geometry, Number & Operations

NCTM Process Standard:
Reasoning & Proof, Communication, Connections, Representation

Specific math content or skill addressed:
Measurement, comparison, mental math

Component:
Activity

Materials needed:
None

Preparing students for success:
Students should have experience converting basic units of measure, such as yards into feet and feet into inches.

Students should be familiar with right, acute, and obtuse angles.

Vocabulary:
Less than, more than, greater than, fewer, difference, sum, equals, estimate, about, and all measurement nomenclature

How to do it:

■ Begin with a simple approximation such as placing your hands approximately twelve inches apart and announcing *"My hands are about twelve inches apart. What's another way we can describe how far apart my hands are?"* Possible responses might be:

✳ *"They are a foot apart."*

✳ *"They're ⅓ of a yard apart."*

✳ *"They are three inches less than fifteen inches apart."*

✳ *"They are two more inches than ten inches apart."*

■ Ask the students to show what six inches apart would look like. Then ask, *"What's the difference between the distance between your hands and my hands?"* Possible responses might be:

✳ *"Our hands are six inches less apart than yours."*

✳ *"Your hands are twice as far apart as ours."*

■ Place one of your hands about two feet off the ground and ask the students how far they think your hand is from the ground. Instruct them to each put one hand half as far as yours off the ground; then have them place a hand one fourth as far off the ground. Finally, tell them to place a hand three fourths as far off the ground.

■ Challenge the students with scaling. Place your hands twelve inches apart, and declare they are a mile apart. Ask the students to show what their hands might look like if they were ½ mile apart or two miles apart.

■ Create an angle with your torso and arm. Start by showing the students a right angle by holding your arm horizontal to the ground. Ask students what makes this a right angle. Have them make one too. Challenge them to use any parts of their bodies. Prompt them to move their right angles into acute angles, then obtuse angles.

■ Finally, you can run in place and declare you are running fifty miles an hour. Instruct the students to run half as fast. Ask them *"How fast are you going?"* Then tell them to run twice as fast and ask them *"Now how fast are you going?"*

Grade Level

3

Clock Check-In

NCTM Content Standard:
Data Analysis & Probability

NCTM Process Standard:
Representation

**Specific math content
or skill addressed:**
Time

Component:
Morning message

Materials needed:
Message chart (for the
morning message)

**Preparing students
for success:**

Students should have
some prior experience
with telling time.

Sometimes students like to
show how grown up they are
by saying they have a very late
bedtime. Be sure to discuss
how to keep everybody's
feelings safe as the class
shares bedtimes.

Vocabulary:
Time, earlier, later, half past,
quarter past, quarter till/to

How to do it:

- Post some version of the message below.

> Dear Self-Aware Students!
>
> Over the past few months we have talked continuously about ways to best take care of ourselves. Getting 60 minutes of daily physical activity is sometimes hard, but many of you have managed it! Also, many of you are eating at least 6 fruits or vegetables a day. It's also critical to get a good amount of sleep. Neuroscientists say that people your age need no less than 10 hours of sleep each night. I wonder how you're doing with that challenge!
>
> Below I've drawn two clocks. The clock on the left is where you'll put your initials next to the time you went to bed. The clock on the right is for you to record the time you woke up this morning. We'll spend some time at the end of Morning Meeting to discuss what we have learned about our collective sleeping habits!
>
> Bedtime Clock   Wakeup Clock
>
>

- After reading the message as a class, lead a discussion about the data they've collected. You might ask *"Who sleeps the most?"* or *"How many of us have the same bedtime?"*

112

Make a stem and leaf graph that plots out the data and ask the students to make inferences about their collective bedtimes and wakeup times. For example, one of your graphs may look like this:

6:00	X X X X
6:15	X X
6:30	X X X X X X
6:45	X
7:00	X X X X X X
7:15	X
7:30	X

Coin Flip Probability

NCTM Content Standard:

Probability

NCTM Process Standard:

Reasoning & Proof

**Specific math content
or skill addressed:**

Prediction, probability,
data analysis

Component:

Activity

Materials needed:

Enough coins for every
two students to have one

Prepared forms for recording
the flips (see sample)

**Preparing students
for success:**

Students should have
experience with probability.
This activity can also be an
introduction to a unit on
probability.

Vocabulary:

Probability, data, likelihood

How to do it:

- All students are paired up.

- Each pair executes twenty coin flips (each student gets ten flips) and tallies the data on their form using hash marks.

Each pair's form:

Heads	Tails

- Record the data from each pair on a large chart by going around the circle.

Class's overall form:

	Heads	Tails
Pair 1		
Pair 2		
Pair 3		
Pair 4		

- Lead a discussion with the students about the class's data. For example, you might ask:

  ❋ *"What do you notice about these two columns of numbers?"*

  ❋ *"Why do you think the numbers are so similar?"*

  ❋ *"What do you think might make us get heads (or tails) a lot more often?"*

VARIATION:

Use a pair of dice instead of a coin, updating the form to use eleven columns instead of two.

Digit Pop

NCTM Content Standard:

Number & Operations

NCTM Process Standard:

Communication,
Connections

**Specific math content
or skill addressed:**

Counting

Component:

Activity

Materials needed:

None

**Preparing students
for success:**

Students should have practice
with skip counting.

How to do it:

■ Announce the skip count number and the pop number.

■ The students skip count around the circle. When the pop number comes up in the ones place, the student says "Pop!" instead of the number and pops up into a standing position. For example, if the skip number is two and pop number is eight, the flow would be as follows: *"2, 4, 6, Pop!, 10, 12, 14, 16, Pop!, 20, 22, 24, 26, Pop! . . ."* The game continues around the circle until all are standing.

■ Play another round, changing the pop number and the skip number. This time, the students sit back down when they pop.

■ Depending on the class's achievement levels, have students pop when the pop number comes up in either the ones or tens place.

■ During the activity, or after it, discuss strategies for playing this game. For example, ask the students *"How did you know when to pop?"* They might say:

✳ *"I just listened really carefully for the pop number."*

✳ *"I counted ahead."*

✳ *"The pop number is pretty big, so I knew I could concentrate on the skip counting for a while."*

Dimensions in the Bubble

How to do it:

- Before writing the message, determine the dimensions of five common items in the classroom and make a sheet like the example below.

> **Scavenger Hunt Sheet:**
>
> A) Length of 4 feet: _____
>
> B) Circumference of 1 foot and 3 inches: _____
>
> C) Width of 3 decimeters: _____
>
> D) Perimeter of 42 centimeters: _____
>
> E) Area of 24 square feet: _____

- Post some version of the message below.

> Dear Measuring Mathematicians!
>
> Our measurement unit has given us an opportunity to refine many of our math skills. I have identified five items from our room and have listed their dimensions in the bubble below. All of the items are ones we use regularly. Use the scavenger hunt sheet below the easel to record your findings. There may be more than one correct answer for each blank.
>
> Bring your recordings to circle for Morning Meeting. We'll discuss the group's findings at the end of the meeting.
>
> > A) Length of 4 feet
> > B) Circumference of 1 foot and 3 inches
> > C) Width of 3 decimeters
> > D) Perimeter of 42 centimeters
> > E) Area of 24 square feet

NCTM Content Standard:

Measurement, Geometry

NCTM Process Standard:

Connections, Communication

Specific math content or skill addressed:

Measurement

Component:

Morning message

Materials needed:

Message chart (for the morning message)

Scavenger hunt sheet (see sample)

Preparing students for success:

Students should have prior experience with measurement.

Following these directions might take awhile, so this activity works best if students are in the classroom well before Morning Meeting.

Vocabulary:

Measure, record, length, width, circumference, perimeter, area, inches, feet, centimeters, decimeters

■ Coach the students as they move about recording their findings.

■ After reading the message as a class, discuss the students' work. For example, after students share items they found that fit each measurement, you might ask:

✳ *"What do you notice about the objects we found?"*

✳ *"What strategies did you use to find your objects?"*

✳ *"How many people used addition in this scavenger hunt? How?" "Did anyone use subtraction? How did you use it?" "Did you use multiplication?" "Who used another math skill?"*

✳ *"What surprised you in this activity?"*

EXTENSIONS DURING A LATER MATH LESSON:

■ Revisit this format and have students find new items.

■ Have students create their own scavenger hunt sheet.

Double This

How to do it:

- This activity may take several days to teach depending upon how quickly students catch on to the words and motions.

- First, teach students the chant with a variety of numbers:

    Double, double, _____, _____ (insert number in blank)
    Equals, equals, _____, _____ (insert product of doubling number
                                  in first blank here)
    Double _____ equals _____,
    Double, double _____ (first number), _____ (second number).

    Sample Round 1:

    Double, double, 1, 1,
    Equals, equals 2, 2,
    Double 1 equals 2,
    Double, double 1, 2.

    Sample Round 2:

    Double, double, 2, 2,
    Equals, equals 4, 4,
    Double 2 equals 4,
    Double, double 2, 4.

- Once students are comfortable with the chant, teach them the hand motions by having them do them in the air in front of them.

- Once they are comfortable with those motions, model and have them practice doing them with a partner:

Double, double	Tap pinkie side of fists twice against side of partner's fists
1, 1,	Tap palms twice against partner's palms
Equals, equals	Tap pinkie side of fists twice against side of partner's fists
2, 2,	Tap back of hands twice against back of partner's hands
Double	Tap pinkie side of fists once against side of partner's fists
1	Tap palms once against partner's palms
Equals	Tap pinkie side of fists once against side of partner's fists
2	Tap back of hands once against back of partner's hands
Double, double	Tap pinkie side of fists twice against side of partner's fists
1	Tap palms once against partner's palms
2	Tap back of hands once against back of partner's hands

VARIATION:

If students are ready mathematically, have them change "double" to "triple" and adjust the words and motions accordingly.

NCTM Content Standard:
Number & Operations

NCTM Process Standard:
Problem Solving

Specific math content or skill addressed:
Addition, multiplication

Component:
Activity

Materials needed:
None

Preparing students for success:
Students need to have practice with clapping games that involve partners.

Students need to have prior experience adding or doubling numbers.

This activity will work best closer to the end of the year. Students may first enjoy playing the simpler version of Double This from *Energizers! 88 Movement Activities That Refresh and Refocus, K–6.*

Vocabulary:
Double, how much

Equations and Pictures

NCTM Content Standard:

Number & Operations

NCTM Process Standard:

Problem Solving,
Communication,
Representation,
Connections

**Specific math content
or skill addressed:**

Mathematical description

Component:

Morning message

Materials needed:

Note cards and something
to draw with

Message chart (for the
morning message)

**Preparing students
for success:**

Do this message after
a conceptual unit on
multiplication.

Vocabulary:

Multiplication, story
problems, arrays

How to do it:

■ Post some version of the message below.

Dear Students!

We've been working hard through our unit on multiplication. Below I've listed three equations using multiplication. Scan the three equations and think about which one you could represent best pictorially. I posted an example for the first one. Feel free to use any picture that gives meaning to the equation. Use your experiences over the last few weeks to help you.

$3 \times 4 = 12$ $2 \times 10 = 20$ $6 \times 4 = 24$

XXXX

XXXX

XXXX

■ After reading the message as a class, bring attention to the different ways the equations were represented and the stories that can be told using them. You may say *"Here is a picture of three boys each holding four balloons. What would a story problem sound like for this picture?"* or *"There are six dogs. Each dog has four bones. How many bones are there in all?"*

VARIATION:

When studying a unit on fractions, list three fractions and have students create pictures to match the fraction.

EXTENSION DURING A LATER MATH LESSON:

Have students practice writing story problems for the equations and pictures shown on the message during a later math block.

Examining Temperatures

NCTM Content Standard:

Data Analysis & Probability,
Measurement

NCTM Process Standard:

Reasoning & Proof,
Communication

**Specific math content
or skill addressed:**

Graphs & diagrams,
prediction, estimation

Component:

Morning message

Materials needed:

Message chart (for the
morning message)

**Preparing students
for success:**

Students should have some
experience with line graphs.

Vocabulary:

Line graph, high, low,
prediction, estimation

How to do it:

- Post some version of the message below. Draw in a line graph showing the last four days' low temperatures.

> Dear Meteorologists,
>
> The temperature has dropped over the last 4 days. Playing outside has been limited because of the cold temperature and excessive wind. I heard the weatherperson say last night that the windchill factor brought the temperature down to −2 degrees. Brrrrr!
>
> The graph below shows the lowest temperature for each of the last 4 days. The weatherperson says that the pattern of decreasing temperatures will continue. What do you predict the coldest temperature will be tomorrow?
>
>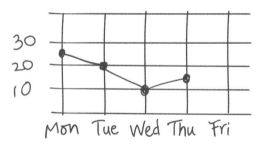

After the class reads the message, lead a discussion about the predictions the students made. Questions you could ask include:

❋ *"Looking at our line graph, what would you say the range of numbers is? What's the high number? The low number?"*

❋ *"What pattern do you see in our graph?"*

✳ *"What's your estimation of how much the temperature has dropped in total over the last four days?"*

✳ *"What's your predication for tomorrow's low?"*

■ Tell them that the class will check tomorrow to see how accurate the predictions were.

EXTENSION DURING A LATER MATH LESSON:

The next day, present the graph during math with the actual low temperature and discuss the various predictions/estimations the students recorded.

How Long Will It Bounce?

NCTM Content Standard:

Number & Operations

NCTM Process Standard:

Communication, Connections, Problem Solving, Representation

Specific math content or skill addressed:

Time

Component:

Morning message

Materials needed:

Bouncy balls

Stopwatches or a clock with a second hand

Message chart (for the morning message)

Preparing students for success:

Students should be able to bounce a ball carefully without supervision.

Vocabulary:

Time, add, sum, data, range, high, low

How to do it:

■ Post some version of the message to the right.

■ After reading the message and examining the data, see if the class can estimate the total amount of time. You could say:

✳ *"What's your estimate of how much time collectively all the balls bounced?"*

✳ *"What would be a good strategy for adding up all the recorded numbers to determine a sum?"*

✳ *"Let's imagine that all the balls bounced twice as long. How long would your ball have bounced? Chat with a partner about that. How long would all of the balls have bounced collectively? What's one strategy for figuring that out?"*

EXTENSION DURING A LATER MATH LESSON:

■ Make a stem and leaf graph to show the data.

Dear Playful Students!

Find a partner and take one bouncy ball. Take turns dropping the ball from the height of the message chart, and time each bounce using the stop watches in the bucket below to see how long until the ball stops bouncing and rolling. Before you start, make a prediction and share it with your partner. Then record the actual time in the space below.

Amount of time ball bounced:

How Much Money?

NCTM Content Standard:

Number & Operations

NCTM Process Standard:

Reasoning & Proof,
Problem Solving

**Specific math content
or skill addressed:**

Money, addition, estimation

Component:

Activity

Materials needed:

Real or play coins (pennies,
nickels, dimes, quarters)

Plastic bags

**Preparing students
for success:**

Students should have
experience working
with money.

Vocabulary:

Estimation, money
denominations, add

How to do it:

- Before class, prepare baggies of coins: one baggie for every two students. Each baggie should contain some of each type of coin.

- Pair up the students and give each pair a baggie. Each pair examines the bag without opening it, estimates the amount they believe the bag contains, and announces their estimate while you record the information on a chart.

- Each pair quickly estimates the sum of all the estimates listed on the chart and reports their estimated total to the group.

- Each pair opens their bag and counts the money, reporting the exact amount while you record it on the chart next to the estimates.

- Lead a discussion of the estimates and the actual amounts. You might ask questions such as:

  ✳ *"What do you notice about our estimates versus our actual amounts?"*

  ✳ *"How did you make your estimate?"*

  ✳ *"How did you count your money?"*

- Each pair quickly estimates the sum of all the actual amounts listed on the chart.

- Lead a discussion about this work, again asking questions such as:

  ✳ *"What did you notice about our estimates and about the total amount of money our class has?"*

  ✳ *"How did you make your estimate?"*

VARIATION:

As the school year progresses, increase the amount of money in each bag.

EXTENSION DURING A LATER MATH LESSON:

Have the students find the sum of the estimates and the sum of the actual amounts.

Isosceles Triangle Message

NCTM Content Standard:

Geometry

NCTM Process Standard:

Representation

**Specific math content
or skill addressed:**

Identifying shapes

Component:

Morning message

Materials needed:

Message chart (for the
morning message)

**Preparing students
for success:**

Students should have some
prior experience with
polygons and specifically
with isosceles triangles.

Vocabulary:

Polygon, isosceles, triangle

How to do it:

■ Post some version of the
message to the right. On the
message, draw a large isosceles triangle that is made up
of smaller isosceles triangles.
The base of the triangle will
have four isosceles triangles
going across. The subsequent
rows will have three, two, and
then finally one (see the diagram for an example).

■ After reading the message as
a class, discuss the different
triangles that can be found in
the drawing. Tell the students
they'll be working in teams later
to identify as many triangles as
they can.

VARIATION:

Revisit this format throughout
the school year using quadrilaterals, hexagons, and other
polygons.

Dear Mathematicians,

Our exploration of polygons for
our geometry unit has greatly
sharpened our skills. You have
shown a tremendous improve-
ment in your ability to identify
various polygons—specifically
triangles. Take a keen look at
the isosceles triangle drawn
below. How many different
triangles can you identify?

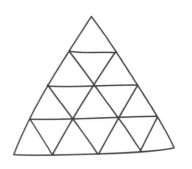

EXTENSION DURING A LATER MATH LESSON:

Put the students in teams of four. Give each team a folder with twenty copies
of the triangle you drew on the message. Have each team of students work
for ten minutes to shade in the different triangles they identify, one per page.
Then have the students form a circle, and each team contributes a shaded
page to a giant chart until all possibilities are shown.

Magical Mystery Machine

NCTM Content Standard:

Number & Operations,
Algebra

NCTM Process Standard:

Communication,
Reasoning & Proof

**Specific math content
or skill addressed:**

Addition, subtraction,
multiplication, division
(as appropriate)

Component:

Activity

Materials needed:

A ball that's easy to catch

Chart, markers (optional)

**Preparing students
for success:**

Students should be familiar
with whichever operation(s)
you plan to use.

Students should have had
practice with the ball-toss
greeting/activity so that they
can toss accurately and not
focus so much on the ball.

Vocabulary:

Depending on the operations
you use: adding, subtracting,
multiplying, dividing,
doubling, etc.

How to do it:

■ Tell the students that in a minute, you're going to turn into the Magical
Mystery Machine. The class will feed you a number, and you're going to
pop out a different number. The group's job is to figure out how you're
changing the numbers (you will apply the same change each time).

■ Toss the ball to a student, who will say *"I give you ____"* and toss the ball
back to you. You say back *"I give you ____."* (An alternate wording could
be *"In goes____"* and *"Out comes ____."*) For example, perhaps you
have decided that the function will be "add seven." You toss the ball to a
student, who says *"I give you ten,"* then tosses the ball back to you. You
announce *"I give you seventeen."*

■ Students must wait until three exchanges have occurred before offering
a guess at the change you're making, even if they suspect they know the
change.

EXTENSIONS DURING A LATER MATH LESSON:

■ Play again later, asking students what went on in their brains as they figured out what the "machine" was doing.

■ If necessary, show the "in" and "out" numbers on paper, with a column
for the "in" numbers and a column for the "out" numbers, or a picture
of a number going into a machine with a different number coming out.
Ask the students how they can get from the "in" number to the "out"
number. They might say *"I can count up"* or *"It looks like you double
the 'in' number."*

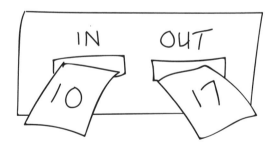

■ Challenge the students to write a number sentence representing what
happens to various numbers as they go through the Magic Mystery
Machine. For example: 10 + 7 = 17.

■ Put the students in pairs or small groups to play the game, with individuals taking turns being the Magic Mystery Machine.

125

Make Ten

NCTM Content Standard:

Number & Operations,
Algebra

NCTM Process Standard:

Communication,
Reasoning & Proof

**Specific math content
or skill addressed:**

Addition

Component:

Greeting or activity

Materials needed:

Pairs of index cards with
numbers 0 to 10, enough
for everyone in the class

**Preparing students
for success:**

Students should have
practice with adding
numbers to make ten.

If done as a greeting,
students should have
practice with mingling.

Vocabulary:

Addends, sum

How to do it:

■ Pass out cards randomly to students. (If you have an odd number of students, sit out so that everyone will have a match.) The object is to match two cards that added together make ten.

■ If this activity is used as a greeting, tell students that their task is to mingle and compare numbers with others until they find their pair (0 and 10, 1 and 9, 2 and 8, etc.) Once they have found their pair, they should stop and greet that person with a handshake.

■ If used as an activity, students should simply find their pair as quickly as they can. Challenge the students to find their pair in a certain amount of time. See if you can beat your record!

VARIATION:

Play the game with different combinations, or different operations such as multiplication, depending on what mathematical skills the class is working on.

EXTENSIONS DURING A LATER MATH LESSON:

■ Play this game as a warm-up activity for a more complicated mathematical activity in which students will use the strategy of looking for numbers to make ten rather than simply adding the numbers as they come to them.

■ Talk more with the students about why it helps to know these facts by heart. With students' input, make a chart of math facts. For example:

If I know ...	Then I know ...
$1 + 9 = 10$	$10 + 90 = 100,\ 100 + 900 = 1000$
$2 + 8 = 10$	$20 + 80 = 100,\ 10 - 8 = 2,\ 100 - 80 = 20$
$3 + 7 = 10$	$30 + 70 = 100,\ 3000 + 7000 = 10000$

3

Marble Probability

NCTM Content Standard:
Probability

NCTM Process Standard:
Representation,
Communication

**Specific math content
or skill addressed:**
Prediction, probability,
data analysis

Component:
Activity

Materials needed:
Enough shakable paper bags
for every two students

Marbles of three different
colors (ten of one color, five
of another, and three of the
third) for each bag (or use
counters or color tiles
instead of marbles)

Prepared forms for recording
the colors pulled

Chart

**Preparing students
for success:**
Students should have
experience with probability.
This activity can also be an
introduction to a unit
on probability.

Vocabulary:
Probability, data

How to do it:

■ Place the marbles in paper bags. Do not tell the students the breakdown of colors for each marble.

■ Pair up the students and give each pair a bag.

■ Each pair of students should shake the bag, pull out a marble, and tally the color of the marble on the prepared form. After tallying, the students should put the marble back in the bag.

■ Each pair executes twenty pulls and records their data.

■ You record the data from each pair on a large chart by going around the circle.

■ Inform the group that they will be looking at the data they collected later during math and should think about what they noticed.

VARIATION:

Use different items or different amounts of an item.

EXTENSIONS DURING A LATER MATH LESSON:

During math class, discuss the data on their tally sheets. For example, you might ask:

■ *"Which color was pulled most often? Why do you think that happened?"*

■ *"How many more times was blue* (if blue was the most often pulled) *pulled than yellow* (if yellow was the least often pulled)? *What does that tell you about what's in the bags?"*

■ *"Find another pair of students and compare tally sheets. What would you guess about what's in your two bags based on the tally sheets?"*

■ *"If you had to guess what color you'll pull right now if I asked you to pull again, what would you guess? Why?"*

Eventually, reveal the color distribution in the bags and ask students their thoughts about how their guesses of the bags' contents compared with the actual contents.

Mental Math Pushups

NCTM Content Standard:

Number & Operations

NCTM Process Standard:

Problem Solving

**Specific math content
or skill addressed:**

Mental math

Component:

Activity

Materials needed:

Prepared lists of expressions.
For the first list, use a list
you think students can have
success with so they can
assimilate the process. Then
increase the difficulty by
creating a second more
challenging list. See the
example to the right.
(Note that the second list
contains multiplication
towards the end.)

**Preparing students
for success:**

Students need to be able
to work in pairs.

Vocabulary:

Plus, minus, times, add,
subtract, equals

How to do it:

- Have the prepared list of expressions displayed, but cover up all but the first expression.

- Show the students the first expression (2 + 2 + 2). Ask them what this expression represents (6).

- Assign partners and tell them they'll work with each other to find the answers to one expression at a time in their heads without using paper, but they must not announce the answers until you give the signal.

- Uncover the second expression on the list and give the class time to work out the answer in their heads. When everyone is ready, ask for the answer. The students should give the answer simultaneously.

- Repeat the process. To build confidence, begin with simpler expressions such as 3 + 3 + 3, 5 + 5 + 5, and 10 + 10 + 10. As the game goes on, the expressions can become more difficult.

First Attempt List	Second Attempt List
2 + 2 + 2	10 + 10 + 10
3 + 3 + 3	100 + 10 + 10
5 + 5 + 5	100 + 10 + 5
10 + 10 + 10	100 + 10 − 5
10 + 10 − 1	2 × 2 + 1
10 + 10 − 5	5 × 5 + 1
10 + 10 − 10	10 × 10 + 1

Message Relationships

NCTM Content Standard:

Number & Operations

NCTM Process Standard:

Connections

**Specific math content
or skill addressed:**

Number relationships

Component:

Morning message

Materials needed:

Message chart (for the
morning message)

**Preparing students
for success:**

No special preparation
is necessary.

Vocabulary:

Relate, relationship,
language around time,
fractions, and more

How to do it:

■ Post some version of the message below.

Dear Math Masters,

Over the past few months we have examined many different math concepts. I've listed some numbers that in some
way relate to our team and the work we do. Spend some
time before Morning Meeting thinking about how these
numbers relate to us. At the end of the meeting we'll
discuss what you noticed. I've started you off with an
example.

Example: 10—the number of greetings we have in our list
of "Morning Meeting Greetings We Know"

24

8:40

$\frac{1}{2}$

94

343

You should be sure to choose numbers that actually do have meaning for
the class.

■ After reading the message as a class, ask the students how they think the
numbers listed relate to them and the work they do. Possible responses
include:

❋ *"343 is the number of books we've read as a class."*

❋ *"Ninety-four is the number of days we've been in school."*

❋ *"$\frac{1}{2}$ represents the fraction of girls in the class."*

CONTINUED ▶

Message Relationships

✳ *"¹/₂ is how many days of school we have left out of the whole school year."*

✳ *"Twenty-four is the total number of students in our room."*

✳ *"Twenty-four is one less than the number of writing journals in our room."*

✳ *"8:40 is when we begin Morning Meeting every day."*

VARIATION:

Revisit this format throughout the school year using different numbers.

EXTENSION DURING A LATER MATH LESSON:

Refer back to this morning message when discussing patterns and relationships in numbers.

Multiplying Us

How to do it:

- Roll the die, or have a student do so. Put that number of Hula-hoops in the middle of the circle.

- Roll the die again. Ask that number of students to step into each Hula-hoop. (For instance, if you rolled a three, each Hula-hoop would need to have three students in it.) If you run out of students, use small stuffed animals or other objects to complete the process.

- Write a sentence to represent the problem you solved: 3 groups of 4 students equals 12 students. If you have already introduced the concept of multiplication, write a number sentence: $3 \times 4 = 12$.

- Repeat the process several times.

EXTENSION DURING A LATER MATH LESSON:

Have students complete a similar process individually. When they roll the first die, they draw that number of circles. When they roll the second die, they draw that many stars inside each circle. Then they figure out their totals.

NCTM Content Standard:

Number & Operations

NCTM Process Standard:

Problem Solving

Specific math content or skill addressed:

Multiplication, sorting/grouping

Component:

Activity

Materials needed:

One die

Six small Hula-hoops or circles of yarn big enough for several students to stand inside

Small stuffed animals or other objects

Chart

Preparing students for success:

Students will need some experience with activities that require them to move around the center of the circle.

Let students know that they are going to use themselves to show some multiplication problems. Tell the students that not everyone will get to participate in each round, but all of them will eventually get a turn. Remind them of ways they can participate (calculating the total in their heads, for instance) and expected behavior when they're not actively participating.

Vocabulary:

Groups, sets

Pica Ferme Nada

NCTM Content Standard:

Number & Operations,
Algebra

NCTM Process Standard:

Communication,
Reasoning & Proof

**Specific math content
or skill addressed:**

Number relationships

Component:

Activity

Materials needed:

Chart

**Preparing students
for success:**

Students should be
comfortable working with
the size of the numbers you
are using (i.e. three-digit
numbers). It helps if they
have had some experience
playing other guessing
games, such as 20 Questions
or Guess My Number
(page 84).

Vocabulary:

Range, ones, tens, hundreds,
thousands, ten-thousands,
etc. (as appropriate),
digit, strategy

How to do it:

- Choose a three-digit number, write it down secretly, and put it where you can access it but students cannot see it.

- Set up the board like the example to the right (the blanks stand for the digits in the secret number).

0 1 2 3 4 5 6 7 8 9

— — —

Guesses:

- Ask for a random guess to start the group off and record it on the board. Then, underneath each number, note whether the number is a "pica," a "ferme," or a "nada" (indicate this with a P, F, or N):

  ✳ **Pica** means the right number but not in the right place.

  ✳ **Ferme** means the right number in the right place.

  ✳ **Nada** means that number is not in the secret number at all.

- For example, if the secret number is 562 and the guess is 268, you would assign the 2 a P, the 6 an F, and the 8 an N.

- Ask the student who guessed *"What does that tell us?"* If a student needs help, allow him or her to call on somebody else to help out. In the above case, a student who knows the game well would be able to say *"There is a two in our number, but it's not in the hundreds place; there is a six in the tens place, and there is no eight in our number."* As they say this, fill in the six.

- Use the numbers 0–9 to help students keep track of numbers they have tried out: cross a number out when it is determined that it's not in the secret number, circle a number that has been tried and is in the number somewhere, and cross the circle out once the number has been put in the right spot.

■ Continue asking students for guesses until the group has successfully worked together to determine the secret number.

■ Some students will develop strategies more quickly than others. Encourage them in the use of their strategies, allowing time for others to observe and pick up on these strategies themselves. When it seems appropriate, ask students *"I can tell you had a strategy going into that guess. Can you tell the group what it was?"*

VARIATION:

Play with a number as high as the students can go, although three-, four-, and five-digit numbers work best.

EXTENSIONS DURING A LATER MATH LESSON:

■ Have students play with a partner or small group on small whiteboards or a premade recording sheet once they are all very familiar and comfortable with the game.

■ When students are really comfortable with this game, they often ask if they can take over for you and lead the game. This definitely takes practice!

Grade Level

3

Piloting

NCTM Content Standard:

Number & Operations

NCTM Process Standard:

Communication,
Representation

**Specific math content
or skill addressed:**

Navigational directions,
estimation, measurement

Component:

Activity

Materials needed:

Color tile to use as a marker

**Preparing students
for success:**

Students need to be able
to work as a team and listen
to each other effectively.

Because one student will
stay blindfolded, this activity
requires a safe environment.
Not all students will want to
be blindfolded. This activity
might work best late in the
year when the class has
built up a lot of trust.

Vocabulary:

Left, right, forwards,
backwards, inches, feet,
diagonally, laterally

How to do it:

- Place the color tile in a random spot in the middle of the circle of students. Tell the students that one of their classmates will pretend to be a pilot and will depend upon their directional advice (because the student will be blindfolded) to land a plane (meaning arrive at the colored tile).

- Model with the students, using an unblindfolded volunteer, how to give directional advice to get the volunteer from where she is in the circle to where the color tile is. Use directions like *"Take two steps forward,"* *"Take one step diagonally to the left and front,"* *"Take two steps laterally to the right,"* and *"Take one step forward."* In the end, the directions may be as explicit as *"Move your left foot ½ inch to the left."*

- Begin the activity using a blindfolded student. The students go around the circle giving directions—one direction per student—until the pilot has landed on the color tile. This will require the students to be absolutely accurate in their directions.

- Repeat the activity with a different blindfolded student.

Ruler Around the Room

NCTM Content Standard:

Measurement, Geometry,
Number & Operations

NCTM Process Standard:

Problem Solving,
Communication

**Specific math content
or skill addressed:**

Measurement,
identifying shapes

Component:

Morning message, sharing

Materials needed:

Rulers

Pencils and paper

String

Message chart (for the
morning message)

**Preparing students
for success:**

Students should have
some prior experience with
measuring, recording, and
identifying shapes.

Following these directions
might take awhile, so this
activity works best if students
are in the classroom well
before Morning Meeting.

Vocabulary:

Measure, record, meters,
centimeters

How to do it:

■ Post some version of the message below.

> Dear Students!
>
> Our unit on measurement has made us highly skillful in using the metric system. Around the room are many things that can be measured in various ways.
>
> Try to find something for which you can find the **circumference**. (Use a piece of string to help you with this challenge. String can be found in the art center.) Find another item for which you can measure the **length**. Finally, find an object for which you can measure the **perimeter**. Measure everything using the metric system. Record your information on one of the recording sheets below the easel. Bring your recordings to Morning Meeting and place them behind you. Be prepared to share what you've learned about at least one of your items in an around-the-circle share.

■ Check in with the students as they move about the room.

■ Before sharing, take a minute to model what the sharing will look and sound like, and have the students silently rehearse their sharing. For example, you might say *"One thing I measured is the glass in our door. It's sixty-five centimeters long"* or *"I measured this baseball using string and found that its circumference is about twenty-three centimeters."*

■ Following the sharing, discuss the class's experience. For example:

❋ *"What tools did you use to make your measurements? If you didn't have any tools, could you still guess approximate circumferences, lengths, and perimeters? What are some ways?"*

❋ *"What was hard about taking your measurements? What was easy?"*

CONTINUED ▶

Ruler Around the Room

❋ *"What was the biggest thing someone measured? The smallest?"*

❋ *"Does anyone have another strategy for measuring circumference that they'd like to try next time? Perimeter? Length?"*

❋ *"Does anyone want to estimate what one of the measurements you wrote down would be in inches or feet?"*

VARIATION:

Use U.S. standard measurement instead of metric units.

EXTENSIONS DURING A LATER MATH LESSON:

■ Have students measure parts of the room they haven't measured yet.

■ Have the class sort items they measured by size.

3

Spinner Probability

NCTM Content Standard:

Data Analysis & Probability

NCTM Process Standard:

Connections, Representation

Specific math content or skill addressed:

Prediction, probability, data analysis

Component:

Activity

Materials needed:

Enough spinners for every two students

Prepared forms for recording the spin results (see sample)

Preparing students for success:

Students should have experience with probability. This activity can also be an introduction to a unit on probability.

Vocabulary:

Probability, data, likelihood

How to do it:

■ The students pair up.

■ Each pair executes 20 flicks of the spinner (each student gets 10 flicks) and tallies the data on their form using hash marks. Spinners should be unevenly divided into three blue sections, two red sections, and one yellow section. (The sections could also be marked by an attribute other than color.)

Each pair tallies the data from their spin on a form like the one to the right.

Blue	Red	Yellow

■ Record the data from each pair on a large chart (an example is at the right) by going around the circle.

	Blue	Red	Yellow
Pair 1			
Pair 2			
Pair 3			
Pair 4			

■ Lead a discussion about the class's data. For example, you might ask:

❋ "What do you notice about our data?"

❋ "Why do you think the spinners landed on blue most often?" "On yellow least often?"

❋ "If you wanted the spinner to land on the three colors equally often, what would you do to try to make that happen?"

❋ "What's your estimate of how many times more often the spinner lands on red than on yellow? On blue than on yellow? How did you figure that out?"

CONTINUED ▶

Spinner Probability CONTINUED

✳ *"Let's say your partner always spins hard and you always spin softly. How do you think that would affect the results that you as a pair get?"*

VARIATION:

Acquire or make spinners with more sections and variations.

EXTENSION DURING A LATER MATH LESSON:

Examine the data further during math class. Create a graph of the number of times each pair of students got each color. Challenge the students to predict what will happen if another color is added to the spinner.

Tens

NCTM Content Standard:

Number & Operations,
Data Analysis & Probability

NCTM Process Standard:

Communication

**Specific math content
or skill addressed:**

Counting, estimation

Component:

Activity

Materials needed:

None

**Preparing students
for success:**

Because this activity involves
speaking aloud and trying
to avoid saying a specific
number, students should be
comfortable as a community
and know how to support
one another. It would be best
to do this activity towards
the middle or end of the
school year.

Vocabulary:

Strategy

How to do it:

■ Announce or decide together a target number. Ten is a good number to start with (hence the name of this activity), but any number can be chosen—just not too high. After about fifty, the activity would drag.

■ One student begins by counting by ones. The student has the option of saying just "one," saying "one, two," or saying "one, two, three." The next student continues counting and has the option of adding on the next one, two, or three numbers. The goal is to **avoid** being the one to say the target number. So, one round, with a target number of ten, might sound like this:

Student 1: *"One, two."*
Student 2: *"Three, four, five."*
Student 3: *"Six."*
Student 4: *"Seven, eight, nine."*
Student 5: *"Ten!"*

Note that Student 5 had no choice but to say "ten"—so it is important to recognize this, have a quick laugh or moan together, and to move on quickly. Nobody is considered "out."

VARIATIONS:

■ Play the game using counting by twos, threes, or fives rather than counting by ones (but it would help to have experience playing with ones first). For example, if you were counting by twos and the target number was sixteen, the round might look like this:

Student 1: *"Two, four, six."*
Student 2: *"Eight, ten, twelve."*
Student 3: *"Fourteen."*
Student 4: *"Sixteen!"*

■ If the group is studying fractions or decimals, count by those instead. Also encourage students to play this game in small groups as a quiet waiting game (whispering or talking quietly with a partner).

Things in Groups #1

NCTM Content Standard:

Number & Operations

NCTM Process Standard:

Communication,
Connections

Specific math content or skill addressed:

Multiplication

Component:

Morning message

Materials needed:

Message chart (for the morning message)

Preparing students for success:

Students often do better on this assignment if they have some time to think about it beforehand. Asking them to reflect on it as they leave on the prior day or for homework the night before might be beneficial. For instance, you might write the following as a homework assignment: *"Today we brainstormed things that come in twos, and tomorrow we'll think about things that come in threes, fours, and fives. Look through picture books and talk to your parents, your babysitters, or your siblings, and see if you can think of any things that come in these groups."*

Vocabulary:

Group, set

How to do it:

■ Post some version of the message below.

> Dear Class,
>
> At math time today we are going to continue talking about things that come in groups or sets. You already came up with many interesting things that come in twos (hairy eyeballs!). In the space below, let's keep working on groups as you write one thing that comes in groups of 3, 4, or 5:
>
> 3   4   5

■ A completed message might contain responses like these:

3	4	5
triplets	tires on a car	fingers on one hand
wheels on a tricycle	window panes	toes on one foot
long shots in basketball	legs on a dog or cat	players on a basketball team
legs on a stool	legs on a table	points on a star
sides on a triangle	seasons	
little pigs	corners in a room	
musketeers		

■ During the message portion of the meeting, have students work with these groups by asking questions like *"If I had three tricycles, how many wheels would I have?"* or *"I have two dogs, so how many legs would that be?"* or *"Two teams are playing basketball. How many players are on the court at one time?"* After students respond, follow up by asking *"How did you figure that out?"* Ask a few students to pose their own problems and have some classmates solve those.

VARIATION:

Repeat with higher numbers up to twelve over the course of a few days.

EXTENSION DURING A LATER MATH LESSON:

At math time, have students write or solve multiplication problems of their own using things from the list they created at Morning Meeting.

Algebra Card Game

NCTM Content Standard:

Number & Operations,
Algebra

NCTM Process Standard:

Problem Solving

**Specific math content
or skill addressed:**

Algebra, identifying numbers,
addition, subtraction,
multiplication, division

Component:

Activity

Materials needed:

Premade pairs of cards that
have the same answer when
a variable is applied

Blank cards

Chart with designated
values for variables
(see sample to right)

**Preparing students
for success:**

Students need experience
with reading a chart.

Students should have
experience with replacing
a variable with a value to
determine an answer.

Vocabulary:

Depending on the operation,
addends, difference, factors,
products, equals, equation,
variable as appropriate

How to do it:

■ Each student receives one card. A card might say, for example, 142 + a = ?, and the matching card might say 150 − e = ?

■ Each student replaces the variable on the card with the charted value and then finds the student who has the same answer.

■ The partners use the variables on the chart to create two new cards that have the same answer.

■ Collect all cards, shuffle all the cards and play a second round. Be sure to mix them up and try to have them distributed in a way that the students don't receive the same card they had previously.

VARIATION:

Vary the complexity of the numbers by introducing fractions, decimals, and money as the students' skills develop throughout the school year.

$$a = 2$$
$$b = 3$$
$$c = 4$$
$$d = 5$$
$$e = 6$$

EXTENSIONS DURING A LATER MATH LESSON:

■ Use this activity as an energizer to review skills and also get students moving.

■ Students can help build a supply of decks of cards that carry the class through the year.

Attribution Messages

How to do it:

- Post some version of the message below.

Dear Ready-for-Winter Students,

Old Man Winter is on his way and the trees have deco-
rated our land with beautiful offerings. I have gathered
several bags full of leaves for us to work with during our
math block today. Take a minute to examine the leaves
I've taped to the message, then list words under each leaf
to describe the attributes of the leaves you see.

P.S. I've also placed a variety of leaves on the examination
table. Use a magnifying glass to closely examine those
specimens.

P.P.S. Come to circle ready to discuss how we might sort
the two bags of leaves next to the easel.

NCTM Content Standard:

Data Analysis & Probability,
Measurement

NCTM Process Standard:

Connections, Representation

**Specific math content
or skill addressed:**

Attribution, sorting/
grouping, data analysis,
measurement

Component:

Morning message

Materials needed:

Items to be examined
(in this example, leaves)

Message chart (for the
morning message)

**Preparing students
for success:**

Students should have some
prior experience attributing
characteristics, sorting,
and measuring.

Vocabulary:

Attribution, characteristic,
size, shape, angle,
magnitude, compare

- Before meeting, students interact with the message, listing words that
describe the characteristics of the taped leaves. Make sure you include
a variety of types of leaves on the chart so that students begin to think
about the different characteristics and how they might sort them.

- During the meeting, prompt the class to brainstorm more words that
would describe the taped leaves. You might say *"This is a good list but
let's see if we can come up with even more words to describe each one
of these leaves. Look really carefully at each one."* List the additional
words on the chart.

■ Ask the students to look at all the different words on the chart and think of some categories you could use to sort the leaves in the bag. Possibilities might include by color, by texture, by width, by shape, by tree type, etc. Challenge the students to come up with as many categories as possible.

VARIATION:

Use the same format with other items, such as rocks/minerals, animal bones, shells, or pictures of animals.

EXTENSIONS DURING A LATER MATH LESSON:

■ Have the students measure the leaves in the bags and sort them by size, shades, and shapes. Use a rotation: each student goes to a station to engage in a task, then students switch stations.

■ Make a rubbing of the leaves on newsprint and brainstorm attributes while labeling measurements such as perimeter, area, length, and width.

Bacon and Eggs

NCTM Content Standard:

Number & Operations

NCTM Process Standard:

Connections

**Specific math content
or skill addressed:**

Counting, division

Component:

Activity

Materials needed:

None

**Preparing students
for success:**

Make sure students know
how to appropriately
support classmates who
make a mistake.

Vocabulary:

Multiple, divisible by

How to do it:

■ Decide on two special numbers and announce them to the class (for example, two and five).

■ Students count off around the circle, starting with one. Every time a number is a multiple of one of the special numbers, instead of saying that number, the student will say either "bacon" or "eggs". Alternate "bacon" and "eggs"—if the last one said was "bacon," the student should say "eggs" (and vice versa).

For example, if your special numbers are two and five, your count off might sound like this: *"1, bacon, 3, 4, eggs, bacon, 7, eggs, 9, bacon, 11, eggs, 13, bacon, eggs . . ."*

VARIATION:

Once students become experienced at this activity, try skip counting around the circle.

Bar Graphing Favorites

How to do it:

NCTM Content Standard:

Data Analysis & Probability

NCTM Process Standard:

Representation

**Specific math content
or skill addressed:**

Graphs & diagrams

Component:

Morning message

Materials needed:

Message chart (for the
morning message)

**Preparing students
for success:**

Students should have prior
experience with bar graphs.

Vocabulary:

Graph, least, greatest,
median, total

■ Post some version of the message below (this example has already been partly completed).

Dear Team,

As we continue to explore our hopes and dreams, we are learning a lot about one another. Over the next few days we will work to collect data relating to our favorites. This information will help us get to know one another even better.

Place a check mark above the category that you consider your favorite for the topic expressed in the graph below. Stack your check marks neatly on top of each other!

ANIMALS

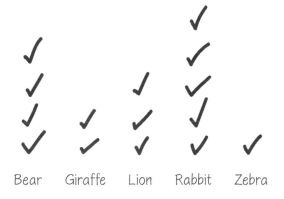

Bear   Giraffe   Lion   Rabbit   Zebra

VARIATIONS:

■ Use the following topics: color, animal, place to go, activity, sport, subject, special, etc.

■ Explore different topics at different times during the year.

CONTINUED ▶

147

Bar Graphing Favorites CONTINUED

EXTENSIONS DURING A LATER MATH LESSON:

Once the data is collected, use it to discuss graphing and data analysis. Ask the class such questions as:

■ *"What appears to be the most popular animal?"*

■ *"How many more people chose rabbit as their favorite over zebra?"*

■ *"Who thinks they can order the favorites from least to greatest?"*

Battery Algebra

NCTM Content Standard:

Number & Operations,
Algebra

NCTM Process Standard:

Communication, Problem
Solving, Connections,
Reasoning & Proof,
Representation

**Specific math content
or skill addressed:**

Algebra, multiplication,
addition

Component:

Morning message

Materials needed:

Batteries of different sizes
(1.5 volt, 9 volt)

Flashlight that requires
a 9-volt battery

Message chart (for the
morning message)

**Preparing students
for success:**

Students should have
experience with the concept
of multiplication.

Vocabulary:

Addends, sum, factors,
products, variables,
multiply, add, equals

How to do it:

■ Before the meeting, tape the 1.5-volt battery to the message chart and place the flashlight next to the message chart.

■ Post some version of the message to the right.

■ After reading the message as a class, lead a discussion about the strategies they used to determine the number of batteries it would take to light up the lightbulb. The discussion could begin with a question like *"How did you go about determining how many batteries it would take?"* Possible responses include:

✳ *"I added up 1.5 until I got 9."*

✳ *"I used guess and check multiplication and multiplied 1 by 6, then ½ by 6, and then added up the two products."*

Dear Electric Students,

Math is all around us. Flashlights can help us understand how math plays a part in turning on a light-bulb. Notice below I've taped a 1.5-volt battery to the message. On the apron of the easel is a flashlight that needs 9 volts of power to light up the lightbulb. Discuss with a friend how many 1.5-volt batteries you think it will take to power on the lightbulb. Come to circle ready to share your thinking.

Extra Thinking Challenge! How many 3-volt batteries would it take to light up the lightbulb?

■ Record the different ways the students solved the problem. In the end the chart may have expressions like these on it:

$1 + 1 + 1 + 1 + 1 + 1 + \frac{1}{2} + \frac{1}{2} + \frac{1}{2} + \frac{1}{2} + \frac{1}{2} + \frac{1}{2}$
$1\frac{1}{2} + 1\frac{1}{2} + 1\frac{1}{2} + 1\frac{1}{2} + 1\frac{1}{2} + 1\frac{1}{2}$
$(6 \times 1) + (6 \times \frac{1}{2})$
$b = 1.5 \ b + b + b + b + b + b$
$b = 1.5 \ 6 \times b$
$(2 \times 1.5) + (2 \times 1.5) + (2 \times 1.5)$

VARIATION:

Change the size of the battery or the amount of voltage needed.

EXTENSION DURING A LATER MATH LESSON:

Get batteries of different sizes and test the amount of voltage needed to light up various lightbulbs.

Coded Messages

NCTM Content Standard:
Data Analysis & Probability

NCTM Process Standard:
Problem Solving,
Connections

**Specific math content
or skill addressed:**
Charts

Component:
Morning message

Materials needed:
Variables chart
Message chart (for the
morning message)

**Preparing students
for success:**
Students should have
some prior experience
with reading charts.

Vocabulary:
Chart, variable

How to do it:

■ Post some version of the message below.

> Dear Math Whizzes!
>
> You will need the attached chart to read the rest of this message. Good luck!
>
> Mr. (z) will be here later with his (x) collection. What do we already know about these (b)? Take a minute to note one thing you already know about these (b) in the space below:
>
>
> I notice you are working (y) on your structures. The (e) and (j) are impressive. Mrs. (d) remarked about the team-work it took to make these structures so impressive. Continue to put your best (r) towards this amazing work.

■ Also, have a chart listing the variables and their meaning. The chart may look something like this:

b animals	r efforts
d Smith	x snake
e precision	y hard
j beauty	z Jones

■ Students plug in the words that correspond with each variable and read the message.

EXTENSION DURING A LATER MATH LESSON:

Have the students create their own coded messages as part of a writing assignment.

Coin Combinations

NCTM Content Standard:

Number & Operations,
Algebra

NCTM Process Standard:

Problem Solving

**Specific math content
or skill addressed:**

Money, counting

Component:

Morning message

Materials needed:

Message chart (for the
morning message)

**Preparing students
for success:**

Students need to be fairly
adept at counting coins.

Vocabulary:

Penny, nickel,
dime, quarter

How to do it:

■ Include some version of the following as a related task on your message:

I have 87 cents. What coins could I have? Let's see how many ways we can figure out!

(Be sure to choose an amount that will lend itself to multiple correct answers.)

■ During the message portion of the meeting, lead students through counting up combinations they wrote. If any combination does not total 87 cents (or whatever target you have chosen), help figure out how to change it so that it does.

■ Ask students *"Do you think we have found all the different ways to make 87 cents? Why or why not?"*

VARIATION:

Ask the inverse question in your message: *"I have nine coins. How much money could I have?"*

EXTENSION DURING A LATER MATH LESSON:

At math time, have students investigate whether they did indeed exhaust all the possibilities for making 87 cents by using a chart like the following:

Quarters	Dimes	Nickels	Pennies
3	1		2
3		2	2
2	3	1	2

Estimate the Amount

NCTM Content Standard:
Number & Operations

NCTM Process Standard:
Problem Solving

Specific math content or skill addressed:
Estimation

Component:
Activity

Materials needed:
Assorted mix of base ten blocks in a paper grocery bag

Preparing students for success:
Students need experience with estimating quickly.

Vocabulary:
Estimation, adding, regrouping

How to do it:

■ Give a grocery bag full of base ten blocks to a student in the circle. The student, on receiving the bag, takes two handfuls of blocks and lays them out in front of him or herself.

■ The student who has taken the blocks announces *"Thumbs up when you're ready,"* and then waits five seconds.

■ After five seconds, the student asks *"Estimation is?"* The entire group calls out how many blocks they think the student has taken.

■ The student makes an exact count of the number of blocks, then passes the bag to the next student. The process is repeated until the bag has gone around the circle (or for as long as time permits).

VARIATION:

Use Cuisenaire rods instead of base ten blocks.

EXTENSIONS DURING A LATER MATH LESSON:

Use this activity to break up a math block.

Estimating and Measuring

NCTM Content Standard:

Measurement

NCTM Process Standard:

Connections, Representation

**Specific math content
or skill addressed:**

Estimation, measurement,
charts

Component:

Morning message

Materials needed:

Items to be measured

Message chart (for the
morning message)

**Preparing students
for success:**

Students should have
some prior experience
with estimation and
measurement.

Vocabulary:

Chart, estimation,
measure, centimeter,
decimeter, length

How to do it:

■ Post some version of the message below.

Dear Champion Students,

Our measurement unit has been full of many great challenges and lots of new learning. I've taped some items to
the chart below. Before coming to the circle, make a
chart in your math journal that lists the items below.
Include columns for an estimated length and an actual
length. Without using any materials, use your eye to
estimate the length of the items and chart your
estimations in metric form. Later today we'll examine
the items closely and find their exact measurement.

Also, later today we'll have time for book share. Be sure
you're ready to give the team an update!

■ Students come to circle and place their math journals behind them until
it's time to read the message.

■ After they read the message as a class, the students examine the charts
they created and share their estimations for each of the items.

■ Lead the exact measuring. A student can come up and measure the items,
or you can do it.

■ Once the exact measurements are made, the students return to their seats
and complete their charts.

CONTINUED

153

Estimating and Measuring

VARIATION:

Use the same format to measure width, perimeter, area of items, or even mass.

EXTENSION DURING A LATER MATH LESSON:

Instead of taking the exact measurement at the meeting, assign the items to groups for math class. Each group can then measure the items and report their findings so all students can complete their charts.

Fencing In an Area

NCTM Content Standard:

Number & Operations,
Geometry

NCTM Process Standard:

Communication, Problem
Solving, Connections,
Reasoning & Proof,
Representation

**Specific math content
or skill addressed:**

Measurement, geometry

Component:

Morning message

Materials needed:

Color tiles (one inch square)

Message chart (for the
morning message)

**Preparing students
for success:**

Students should have
experience with the concepts
of area and perimeter.

Following these directions
might take awhile, so this
activity works best if students
are in the classroom well
before Morning Meeting.

Vocabulary:

Multiply, area, perimeter,
length, width, side,
corner, add, array

How to do it:

■ Post some version of the message below.

> Dear Horticulturists,
>
> I've always wanted to have a garden. I've been thinking
> about how big of a garden I would want to have, and
> I've decided that my garden would be 36 square yards.
> I would also want to fence in my garden to protect my
> crops from hungry rabbits! I need your help with coming
> up with the amount of fencing I'll need to surround the
> perimeter of the garden based on several different rec-
> tangular formats. I've settled on the following arrays as
> a possible design:
>
> $$6 \times 6$$
> $$4 \times 9$$
> $$3 \times 12$$
>
> With a partner, use the color tiles in our math center to
> help you determine the perimeter for each design. Allow
> each color tile to represent one square yard. Come to
> Morning Meeting ready to discuss your findings.

■ After reading the message as a class, lead a discussion with the students
about the strategies they used to determine the perimeter for each rectan-
gular design. (It may help to have each array drawn out on a separate
sheet to aid in the recording of their findings.) Record their thinking for
the math lesson.

VARIATION:

Vary the area or begin the problem with the perimeter, having them determine the area used.

Fencing In an Area

EXTENSIONS DURING A LATER MATH LESSON:

■ Look over your record of the morning message with the class and bring attention to the fact that differently arranged areas with the same square footage have differing perimeters. Ask the students if they see a pattern in how the perimeters change as the lengths and widths of the rectangles change. Share with the class formulas that are used to determine area (l × w) and perimeter (2l + 2w), and show them how these formulas apply to the problem at hand.

■ Have the students design their own gardens where they also use certain amounts of area for certain crops and also leave room for a gardener to tend to the crops.

How Do We Relate?

NCTM Content Standard:

Algebra

NCTM Process Standard:

Communication,
Connections

**Specific math content
or skill addressed:**

Data analysis

Component:

Activity

Materials needed:

Cards that each have a
different number,
one per student

**Preparing students
for success:**

Students must have had
practice explaining the
relationship of a pair of
numbers. For example, for
(5, 25) the relationship could
be expressed with *"Twenty-
five is twenty more than five,"*
"Five is one fifth of twenty-five,"
*"Five multiplied by five is
twenty-five,"* etc.

Vocabulary:

Terms focusing on relationship
such as more than, less than,
multiple of, one of, etc.

How to do it:

■ Each student receives one card with a number on it and holds the card
for all the other students to see.

■ Pair up students. After all the students have been paired up, give them
several minutes to figure out how their numbers relate, then call a pair
of students to share.

■ Be sure to stretch the students to come up with many ways to describe
the relationship. For instance: *"See if you can come up with at least three
(or five or ten) different ways that the two numbers relate to each other."*
Encourage students to use multiple operations in order to do this, such
as *"5 is $\frac{1}{10}$ of 25 doubled."*

■ Repeat this process using as many different students and varying relationships as possible.

VARIATION:

Once students get good at this game, match up three or more students.

How Many Ways

NCTM Content Standard:
Number & Operations

NCTM Process Standard:
Communication, Problem Solving, Reasoning & Proof

Specific math content or skill addressed:
Multiplication, division, addition, subtraction

Component:
Morning message

Materials needed:
Note cards

Pencils

Message chart (for the morning message)

Preparing students for success:
Students must have experience with combining a variety of operations to arrive at an answer (for example, $3 + 2 - 1 + 1 = 5$ and $2 \times (2 + 2) = 8$).

Vocabulary:
Add, subtract, multiply, sum, difference, addend, product

How to do it:

■ Post some version of the message below.

Dear Arithmetic Whizzes,

As the year has progressed, you have learned how to use your many arithmetic skills. I'm challenging you today to use those skills to find ways to arrive at one of the numbers listed below. See if you can use multiplication, division, addition and subtraction in the same expression. Write your expression on a note card and bring it to circle.

77   50   38   99

I have provided two examples for ways to arrive at 100. Here they are:

$(2 \times 25) + 10 + 10 + 40 - 10$ $(^{200}/4) + 40 + 10$

■ After reading the message as a class, have students share the many ways by which to arrive at each of these numbers. Bring attention to the importance of the use of parentheses.

VARIATION:

Change the numbers. Challenge the students with additional criteria such as having to use numbers with decimals or fractions.

EXTENSION DURING A LATER MATH LESSON:

Use this structure for practice with already known or newly introduced skills.

How Tall Would We Be?

NCTM Content Standard:

Measurement, Data
Analysis & Probabiity

NCTM Process Standard:

Reasoning & Proof

**Specific math content
or skill addressed:**

Measurement, charts,
estimation, prediction

Component:

Activity

Materials needed:

Base ten block tens

Chart

Calculators

Note cards

**Preparing students
for success:**

Students must be familiar
with using base ten block
tens to measure.

Vocabulary:

Measure, measurement,
estimating, estimation,
add, sum, height

How to do it:

- Students pair up, and one of them lies down.

- Students measure their lying-down partners in centimeters using the base ten blocks.

- They write their measurements on note cards and tape them to a chart.

- Partners switch roles. Again, the measurers write their results on note cards and tape their cards to the chart.

- Tell students to look at the data on the chart and to use it to make an estimate about how tall the entire class would be. Let students know that you will be asking them to share their thinking about how they came up with their estimate. Chart the class's estimates, going around the circle.

- Ask the students what they notice about the estimates. If prompting is needed, ask specific questions such as *"What numbers show up most frequently?" "What are the highest numbers?" "What are the lowest numbers?"*

- Ask students to describe the estimation strategies they used— *"What method did you use to make your guess?"*—and see how many different strategies you can name as a group.

EXTENSIONS DURING A LATER MATH LESSON:

- Help the students organize the data by listing the heights from least to greatest and then ask additional questions about the data. For example:

  ✳ *"Are there new things that you notice about the data now that it's better organized?"*

  ✳ *"What's the median?"*

  ✳ *"After looking at all of the estimates, what do you predict the answer will be now and why?"*

- Students work with their partners. Using a calculator, they add up all the heights that are written on the cards taped to the chart. After finding the sum, the students come to the circle with their answers. Work through finding the sum using a calculator with the class, and have the students compare their answers with yours. The class discusses what they noticed about how their estimates differed compared with the actual sum.

Make a Line Segment Animal

How to do it:

■ Post some version of the message below.

> Dear Builders!
>
> Our measurement activity has afforded us plenty of opportunities to learn about the things around us. Today at Morning Meeting we will challenge our group creativity and have some fun using line segments. It is your responsibility to cut a piece of string that is one of the following specified lengths: 2 inches, 4 inches, 6 inches, or 8 inches. You must also bring that segment of string to circle with you and place it behind you.
>
> We will be working as a group trying to build a cat with the pieces of string we will all have. Be thinking about how we might be able to do this as a team.

■ Have all the students put their string in front of them.

■ Tell the students to place their pieces of string in the middle of the circle one at a time. Each string must touch another piece of string. The goal is to create something that looks like a cat.

■ After the students have finished placing their strings, the class examines what has been created. Ask the students *"Does it look like a cat? Why or why not?"* Ask whether anyone would like to make any adjustments.

VARIATION:

Have the class create different animals.

EXTENSIONS DURING A LATER MATH LESSON:

■ During math block or another time of the day, challenge the students to cut string, gather in a circle, and create an animal that may relate to a curriculum area. For example, have the students create a butterfly if you're studying insects, or make the shape of a state or country you're studying in geography.

■ Have the students create a structure with certain criteria. For example: *"As a team, build a house that has at least two floors."*

Make a Polygon Animal

NCTM Content Standard:
Geometry

NCTM Process Standard:
Representation

**Specific math content
or skill addressed:**
Identifying shapes,
part/whole relationships

Component:
Morning message, activity

Materials needed:
5 × 8 note cards

Scissors

Message chart (for the
morning message)

**Preparing students
for success:**
Students should have a
working knowledge
of polygons.

Vocabulary:
Polygon, triangle,
quadrilateral, pentagon,
hexagon, corner, angle

How to do it:

■ Post some version of the message below.

> Dear Builders!
>
> With our geometry unit we have examined polygons in many ways. How various polygons exist in nature has been part of our studies. During our activity time at Morning Meeting we will build a dog as a team using polygons. Using scissors and a 5 × 8 note card, create a polygon to bring to Morning Meeting. Place that note card behind you so it is handy for your activity time.
>
> Be thinking about how we could best go about building this dog as a team.

■ Have all the students put their polygons in front of them.

■ Tell the students that they will place their polygons in the middle of the circle one at a time. Each card must touch another card and as a group they should try to create something that looks like a dog.

■ After the students have finished placing their cards, the class examines what has been created. Ask the students, *"Do you think it looks like a dog?"* *"What makes it look like a dog?"* *"What makes it not look like a dog?"* Ask students if there are any adjustments they think could be made to make it look more like a dog. Invite volunteers to make the adjustments.

■ Have a discussion about polygons. You could ask *"What did you notice about the polygon you were using during this activity?"* or *"Was it easy to place or hard, and why?"*

VARIATIONS:

■ Have the class create different animals.

■ Have the students use pattern blocks instead of polygon cards to build the animal.

 CONTINUED

Make a Polygon Animal CONTINUED

EXTENSIONS DURING A LATER MATH LESSON:

■ During math block (or another time of the day), challenge the students to make cards, gather in a circle, and create an animal that may relate to a curriculum area. For example, have the students create a butterfly if you're studying insects, or make the shape of a state or country you're studying in geography.

■ Have the students create a structure with certain criteria. For example: *"As a team, build a house that has at least two floors."*

Making Change for a Dollar

NCTM Content Standard:

Number & Operations

NCTM Process Standard:

Communication,
Connections, Problem
Solving, Representation

**Specific math content
or skill addressed:**

Money

Component:

Morning message

Materials needed:

Coins

Message chart (for the
morning message)

**Preparing students
for success:**

Students should have
experience working
with money.

Vocabulary:

Quarter, nickel, dime,
penny, add, subtract,
times, multiply

How to do it:

■ Post some version of the message below.

> Dear Students!
>
> Money has been a focus in our classroom for a couple
> of weeks. Sometimes you need to change a dollar bill into
> coins. Making change for a dollar is not always easy,
> especially if you have a limited amount of coins. Below I
> have listed two people and the coins they have. Which one
> of the two can make change for a dollar? Be prepared
> to explain why you believe that person can and the other
> person can't. Use the coins in the math center if you like.
>
> | Andy | Michael |
> |------|---------|
> | 3 quarters | 3 quarters |
> | 4 dimes | 4 dimes |
> | 4 pennies | 4 nickels |

■ After reading the message as a class, conduct a discussion. Start with an
open-ended question such as *"So, what do you think about the ability of
Andy and Michael to make change for a dollar?"* Stretch students' thinking
with questions such as *"If you could make only one change to Andy's
collection of coins, what would you change so that he can make change
for a dollar?"* and *"If someone came up to Andy and Michael with one
of those rare $2 bills and asked to change it into coins, could they do it
together? How?"*

VARIATION:

Use different distributions of coins.

Match Card Greeting

NCTM Content Standard:
Number & Operations

NCTM Process Standard:
Problem Solving

Specific math content or skill addressed:
Addition, subtraction, multiplication, division

Component:
Greeting

Materials needed:
Enough premade index cards for each child—half of them should have expressions (for example, 50 – 35 and 99 + 11), and half should have the corresponding answers (= 15 and = 110).

Preparing students for success:
Students must be able to move about the circle safely and find a matching partner.

Vocabulary:
Depending on the operation, addends, difference, factors, products, quotient, dividend, equals, and equation as appropriate

How to do it:

- Give each student a card.

- Students move about trying to find the match for their card.

- When the students find their match, they greet each other. A simple "hello" or "good morning" is fine.

- Students sit with their matching partner in the order of an equation, visible to the rest of the circle. For example, the student with the 50 – 35 card sits to the right of the student with the = 15 card, and the student holding the card with 99 + 11 is seated to the right of the student holding the card with = 110 on it.

- The students announce their equation one at a time going around the circle while holding their cards so all can see.

VARIATION:

Once this structure is in place, increase the complexity by:

- Changing the magnitude of the numbers

- Using decimals or fractions

- Using money

- Using time

- Attempting more difficult operations, such as division

- Using story problems by placing both story problems and equations in the deck: Each card with a story problem matches a card with an equation. For example, one card might have written on it "Three children each read four books. How many books did they read in all?" The matching card would contain the equation "$3 \times 4 = 12$."

EXTENSIONS DURING A LATER MATH LESSON:

- Ask students to get together with their partners and discover other ways to come up with the answer they worked with. For instance, if they have a card that says 2×2 and it matches up with = 4, they can brainstorm ways to find 4 and list them. Their list may have $100 - 96$, $20 \div 5$, $- 4 + 8$, etc.

- Ask students to create cards for future games. A designated time can be set aside where each student can create a deck that contains enough matching sets for each of their fellow students. Before branching into story problem and equation matching, begin this sort of challenge with simpler equations such as $3 + 2 = 5$ or $10 \times 10 = 100$.

Newspaper Connections

NCTM Content Standard:
Number & Operations

NCTM Process Standard:
Connections

**Specific math content
or skill addressed:**
Mathematical description

Component:
Morning message, sharing

Materials needed:
A stack of newspapers

Message chart (for the
morning message)

**Preparing students
for success:**
Students should be able to
articulate a variety of ways
of looking at numbers.

Vocabulary:
There are many possibilities.

How to do it:

■ Post some version of the message below.

> Dear Worldly Mathematicians!
>
> We are surrounded by math in our world. Strong math skills can help us be better consumers of information. Newspapers are loaded with math.
>
> Notice the stack of newspapers next to the easel. Grab a section and scan it for a number. Familiarize yourself with how the number is used. Cut out the number and the surrounding print or pictures and place your cutout behind you when you come to circle. During sharing, you'll have an opportunity to share about the number you've chosen in two sentences or less.
>
> Here are two examples of what your sharing might sound like:
>
> 1) I chose .333. It is the batting average of Derek Jeter.
>
> 2) The number I picked is $\frac{1}{2}$. This is how much off the regular price bananas are selling for at the super-market.

■ Students leave their cutout behind them until it is their turn to share.

■ One at a time, students share their two sentences.

■ After all students have shared, discuss their findings. You can ask questions such as:

✳ *"How easy or hard was it to find a number in the newspaper section you had?"*

✳ *"What did you notice from our sharing today about the different ways that numbers are used in the newspaper?"*

✳ *"What part of the newspaper do you think would have the most numbers? What part of the newspaper do you think would have the fewest numbers?"*

Pass the Deck Operations

NCTM Content Standard:

Number & Operations

NCTM Process Standard:

Problem Solving

**Specific math content
or skill addressed:**

Addition, subtraction,
multiplication, division,
estimation, mental math

Component:

Activity

Materials needed:

A deck of 5 × 8 cards with
equations written on them

**Preparing students
for success:**

Students need experience
with the operations
represented on the cards. For
best results, use equations
familiar to the class.

Vocabulary:

Varies depending on the
operation(s) used

How to do it:

■ Introduce the activity to the class as a group practice of the skills they've been working on. The deck of equation cards is passed around the circle. (Equations might be, for example, 2 + 2 + 2 + 2, 10 + 10 + 10, 100 − 90 + 10, 10 × 10 × 10, or 160 ÷ 40.)

■ Each student, on receiving the deck, takes a card from the top of the deck and displays it to the rest of the class. The student who reveals the card announces *"Thumbs up when you're ready,"* and then waits five seconds. After five seconds, the student asks *"Answer is?"* The entire group calls out what they think the answer is. The student passes the deck to the next student and the process is repeated until the deck has gone around the circle (or for as long as time permits).

VARIATIONS:

■ Make a deck with fractions instead of equations. The students identify the fraction after the prompt *"Fraction is?"*

■ Make a deck with polygons instead of equations. The students identify the polygon after the prompt *"Polygon is?"*

EXTENSION DURING A LATER MATH LESSON:

Use this activity to reinforce skills at different times of the year. Group practice allows for safety and some fun.

Pattern Chanting

How to do it:

NCTM Content Standard:

Number & Operations,
Algebra

NCTM Process Standard:

Connections

**Specific math content
or skill addressed:**

Patterns, estimation,
geometry, place value,
mental math

Component:

Activity

Materials needed:

None

**Preparing students
for success:**

Students must be able to
keep a chant moving along.

Students must have had
practice with mental
math computation.

Vocabulary:

For the entire activity:
Sum, digits, equals, less
than, greater than

While chanting:
Acute angle, obtuse
angle, perpendicular,
parallel, etc.

■ Teach a patterned chant such as Shante Ohm (see *Energizers! 88 Quick Movement Activities That Refresh and Refocus, K–6* for more details). At first, use only two variables and assign a specific movement to each variable. For example, "Shante Shante Ohm Shante Ohm Shante Ohm" represents an AABABAB pattern; you could have the students pat their laps on "Shante" and clap on "Ohm." With minimal practice, students can master this as a team.

■ Once they can do the chant as a team, have the students explain the pattern that exists within the chant.

■ After the students have mastered the chant, have them keep the chant going as you tell them to move/position their bodies in a variety of ways. Do actions such as rotating to the left/right, creating an acute angle with one leg, holding a leg parallel to the ground, or making the back as perpendicular to the floor as possible.

■ After the students master the chant with movement, challenge them to replace "Shante" and "Ohm" with numbers. For example, the chant may be "1 1 2 1 2 1 2." Do a few rounds of this and then ask them what the sum of the digits is (in this example, the sum is 10). The students share how they arrived at their sum. Raise the challenge by choosing harder numbers such as "5 5 6 5 6 5 6" (the sum of these numbers is 38).

■ Another challenge might be to substitute the "Shante" and "Ohm" with numbers and have the students think of the number the string of digits creates. For example, "1 1 2 1 2 1 2" would create the number 1,121,212. "5 5 6 5 6 5 6" would be the number 5,565,656.

EXTENSION DURING A LATER MATH LESSON:

Repeat the activity at a challenge level that's right for the class. If they're ready, change the magnitude of the numbers, use decimals, or use fractions.

Sharing Milk

How to do it:

- Post some version of the message below.

Dear Ready-to-Party Students!

Later today we'll be celebrating all the hard work we've been doing. Our baked goods will have to be washed down with something healthy. I have some milk chilling in the refrigerator. I think that is a good choice.

However, we need to figure out how many gallons of milk we will need to allow for each student in our classroom to have an eight-ounce glass of milk. Below is an empty gallon container and an empty eight-ounce cup. Use a liquid measurement chart to help you figure out the problem. Be ready to explain your reasoning.

Extra thinking . . . How many gallons would we need if everyone was to have 2 eight-ounce glasses? What if each student only wanted $1/2$ of an eight-ounce glass?

- After reading the message, ask the class *"How many gallons do you think we need?"* Ask students to explain why they have come to the conclusions they have.

- Then, using water, show the students the exact number of gallons that would be needed by pouring the number of glasses that equal the number of students in the room into the gallon milk containers.

- Discuss the "extra thinking" part of the message too. For example, you could ask:

  ✳ *"So how many gallons would we need if everyone wanted two eight-ounce glasses of milk?"* and *"How did you get that answer?"*

  ✳ *"Could we write out our thinking in a number sentence? How? What might be another way to write our number sentence?"*

NCTM Content Standard:
Number & Operations

NCTM Process Standard:
Communication, Reasoning & Proof, Connections

Specific math content or skill addressed:
Addition, fractions

Component:
Morning message

Materials needed:
Gallon milk containers
Several 8-oz. cups
Liquid measurement chart
Message chart (for the morning message)

Preparing students for success:
Students should have some experience working with fractions.
Students should be at least somewhat acquainted with liquid measurement and have access to a liquid measurement chart.

Vocabulary:
Estimation, multiply, divide, add, sum, product, quotient

❉ *"What about if everyone wanted only a half glass? How could we go about solving this problem? What would your thinking sound like?"*

❉ *"How could we prove our thoughts?"*

VARIATION:

Alter the size of the glass.

EXTENSION DURING A LATER MATH LESSON:

Save the "extra thinking" question for the math block.

Spider Web

NCTM Content Standard:

Geometry, Measurement

NCTM Process Standard:

Representation

Specific math content or skill addressed:

Identifying shapes, measurement

Component:

Greeting and activity

Materials needed:

A ball of yarn

Strong tape

Preparing students for success:

Students should have prior experience with polygons, perimeter and area.

You should model how to hang on to and use a piece of tape.

Vocabulary:

Geometric nomenclature such as polygons, corners, angles, quadrilateral, pentagon, hexagon, acute, obtuse, parallel

Other math words such as smaller, bigger, larger, greatest, least, compare, and contrast

How to do it:

■ For the greeting:

❋ Pass around pieces of tape and instruct students to attach them to their knees for now.

❋ Begin by greeting a student, taping the end of the ball of yarn to the floor in front of you, and gently rolling the ball across the circle to the child you greeted.

❋ The ball-receiving student greets you back and then tapes the yarn to the floor.

❋ That student then greets another student and rolls the ball to him. This student in turn greets the student who rolled the ball, then tapes the yarn to the floor in front of him. He continues by greeting another student and rolling the ball to her.

❋ The greeting and yarn ball rolling continues until all the students have been greeted and a giant web has been formed in the middle of the circle.

❋ Leave the spider web attached and use it for math class later, or continue on to the activity below.

■ For the activity:

❋ Ask the students an open-ended question, such as *"What do you notice about the web we created?"*

❋ Each student and his or her shoulder partner chat about what they notice.

❋ Model making one succinct comment about the web using math vocabulary. Examples: *"I notice a lot of triangles and quadrilaterals." "I see a huge triangle here and a small one over here." "Look, these lines make a pentagon."*

❋ Going around the circle, students comment on what they see. If you like, you can chart key words.

EXTENSIONS DURING A LATER MATH LESSON:

■ With partners, students return to the web with a piece of chalk and newsprint, and each pair chooses a polygon to make a rubbing of. Returning to their seats, they first estimate the perimeter and maybe even area of their rubbed polygon. After estimating, the students determine the actual perimeter and area.

■ Challenge the students to make a rubbing of a certain kind of polygon. You may want to focus on triangles or quadrilaterals. The focus may be even more specific, such as only acute triangles.

Split the Group

NCTM Content Standard:

Number & Operations

NCTM Process Standard:

Communication,
Representation

**Specific math content
or skill addressed:**

Division

Component:

Activity

Materials needed:

None

**Preparing students
for success:**

Students should be
comfortable working
with division.

Vocabulary:

Divisor, dividend,
quotient, group,
remainders

How to do it:

- Tell the class that they will split up on the basis of a divisor that you announce. The class should create even groups of students based on the divisor, and any remaining students should stand by you. For example, if the class has twenty-five students, you might announce *"Split up using a divisor of four."* Students would form four groups of six, and one child would stand next to you. If you announced *"Split up using a divisor of five,"* the class would form five groups of five, and there would be no remainder.

- Continue to announce different divisors as the students respond accordingly. Repeat the game for as much time is available.

- You may also choose to record the equations for each "split up" and even draw a quick pictorial representation on a chart.

Split Up the Bags

How to do it:

■ Tell the class that each student will be working with a partner and practicing division skills with color tiles in a bag. Assign partners and pass out the materials. Tell the students they're responsible for splitting up their tiles using the divisors listed on the chart (2, 3, 4, 5, 6).

■ The students split up the tiles and record the equation that matches. For example, if a pair of students has thirty-two tiles in their bag, and the number they must split them by is six, they should begin to construct six piles. There will be five tiles in each pile and two remainders. On their sheet, they will then record "$32 \div 6 = 5$, remainder 2." Or, if the divisor is four, they will make four piles of eight with no remainders, and will record "$32 \div 4 = 8$, remainder 0."

■ Monitor the work and give a warning when the time limit is approaching.

■ Have students share what they discovered through this activity. Ask questions such as:

✳ "What was the most challenging thing about this task?"

✳ "What strategies did you use to group the tiles?"

✳ "Did you run into any problems?"

✳ "Were you surprised by anything?"

✳ "Did you discover something you didn't know?"

VARIATION:

Make the divisors more difficult, or increase the number of tiles in the bags.

Things in Groups #2

NCTM Content Standard:

Number & Operations

NCTM Process Standard:

Communication, Connections, Problem Solving, Reasoning & Proof, Representation

Specific math content or skill addressed:

Multiplication

Component:

Morning message

Materials needed:

Message chart (for the morning message)

Separate chart paper list

Preparing students for success:

No special preparation is necessary.

Vocabulary:

Group, multiply, add, product, factor

How to do it:

- Post some version of the message below.

Dear Multiplication Fanatics,

I asked a bus driver yesterday afternoon how many seats there are on one bus. She told me there are 54 seats for students on each bus! I didn't realize there were that many. Then I found myself wondering how many seats there were on all the buses that come to our school in the morning and in the afternoon. Since there are 8 buses, I put my math thinking skills into action. I realized I could figure out the total number by adding 54 + 54 + 54 + 54 + 54 + 54 + 54 + 54 and I came up with 432. I also checked by multiplying 54 by 8.

I'm wondering how many things you know of that come in groups. Think about items that come in groups of 2, 3, 4, 5, 6, 7, 8, 9, 10, 11, and 12. We'll do some more thinking about this at the end of Morning Meeting.

- After reading the message as a class, produce the premade chart (the chart has the numbers 2, 3, 4, 5, 6, 7, 8, 9, 10, 11, 12 going down the left side with room on the right to list items) and have the students name the items they have thought of as coming in the various groups. You may hear that shoes come in twos, eggs come in groups of twelve, baseball players on the field come in groups of nine, soccer players on the field come in groups of eleven, and corners on a septagon come in groups of seven.

- Lead students through some work with multiplication by saying something like *"Since shoes come in twos, and we have twenty-three students in our class, how many shoes on students do we have altogether?"* or *"How many corners are there altogether when there are five septagons?"*

EXTENSION DURING A LATER MATH LESSON:

Have the students write story problems using the information from the chart. An example would be *"A man purchased four dozen eggs. Each dozen cost three dollars. How many eggs did the man buy, and how much did all the eggs cost him?"*

Average Age

NCTM Content Standard:

Data Analysis & Probability, Number & Operations

NCTM Process Standard:

Connections

Specific math content or skill addressed:

Data analysis, averages

Component:

Morning message

Materials needed:

Message chart (for the morning message)

Preparing students for success:

Students should have some prior experience with collecting and organizing data with specific work regarding range, mode, and median.

Vocabulary:

Data, range, median, mean, mode, high, low, youngest, oldest

How to do it:

■ Post some version of the message below.

> Dear Whizzes!
>
> Throughout the year we have celebrated many birthdays. No two people in here are exactly the same age. However, there are some other interesting points about how old you are. On one of the lines below record the number of years and months old you are. Round up the months. If you are nine years old and you were born on February 10, write 9 years 3 months. If you're eight years old and were born on September 22, write 8 years 8 months.
>
> 9 years 3 months   8 years 8 months
> _____   _____   _____   _____
>
> _____   _____   _____   _____
>
> _____   _____   _____   _____
>
> _____   _____   _____   _____
>
> _____   _____   _____   _____

■ After the class reads the message together, lead a discussion about the data they've collected. You may begin the discussion by asking, for example:

✳ *"What do you notice about our data?"*

✳ *"What's the range of our data?"*

✳ *"Where would you say the midpoint or middle of our range is?"*

✳ *"Which month has the most birthdays? Which month has the least?"*

■ As you act as recorder, the class finds the high and low expressions and creates a chronological list.

CONTINUED ▶

Average Age

■ Ask the class how they might calculate the mean of the data. Possible answers include:

✳ *"We know we have to divide by the number of students in the class."*

✳ *"We might be able to convert the dates to numbers."*

✳ *"It's tricky because you're working with twelve months."*

EXTENSIONS DURING A LATER MATH LESSON:

■ After reviewing the data, draw a graph showing the x and y axes on the message chart. The class should help you label each axis and create a title. Plot a few of the dates, then pair up the students and have them plot the entire list. Looking at the plots, ask the students how this organized set of data could help us think about our data. Ask them *"How would looking at plotted data from the beginning have helped us?"*

■ Calculate the mean.

Batting Averages Message

NCTM Content Standard:

Number & Operations

NCTM Process Standard:

Problem Solving,
Connections

**Specific math content
or skill addressed:**

Averages

Component:

Morning message

Materials needed:

Message chart (for the
morning message)

**Preparing students
for success:**

Students should have
prior experience with
calculating averages.

Vocabulary:

Data, average, divide,
dividend, quotient, divisor

How to do it:

■ Post some version of the message below.

Dear Students!

Spring has sprung and you know what that means: it's time
for baseball and softball! I remember the early days of my
own baseball career. It was exciting to keep track of my
batting average throughout the season. Below you'll find
the batting statistics of two different players. The data
is posted as hits per at-bats. Use your calculators to
determine the batting averages for each player after five
games before coming to Morning Meeting.

	Player A	Player B
Game 1	1/3	2/4
Game 2	2/5	2/4
Game 3	1/3	0/5
Game 4	2/3	3/4
Game 5	1/4	3/4

■ After reading the message as a class, ask for volunteers to share their
answers. Redo the calculations in front of the group to verify their
calculations.

VARIATION:

Write a similar message at other times during the year that incorporates other
sporting statistics. Some to consider could be shots made over shots taken,
games won over games played, and sum of times over trials (see page 195).

EXTENSION DURING A LATER MATH LESSON:

Continue to calculate averages for other interests during the math block.
For example, you could calculate averages for the week's temperatures, the
number of books the students have each read, or the amount of time it takes
the class to transition to various activities.

5

Beach Raft Message

How to do it:

- Post some version of the message below.

NCTM Content Standard:

Data Analysis & Probability,
Number & Operations,
Measurement

NCTM Process Standard:

Problem Solving,
Connections

**Specific math content
or skill addressed:**

Measurement, prediction,
data analysis, counting

Component:

Morning message

Materials needed:

Message chart (for the
morning message)

**Preparing students
for success:**

Students should have a
working knowledge of area.

Vocabulary:

Area, space, square feet

> Dear Ready-For-Summer 5th Graders!
>
> Summer is upon us and many of you will be swimming at the local pool. I couldn't help but imagine our entire class out on a raft in the pool . . . that would be neat to say the least. I was wondering a few things though. . . .
>
> 1) Do you think we would all fit? (The raft is 15' × 20'.)
>
> 2) Would we fit more comfortably standing or sitting?
>
> 3) Knowing the dimensions of the raft, how many 5th graders do you think could fit standing on it?
>
> How about sitting on it?

- After reading the message as a class, lead a discussion about these questions. Tell the students that they will be running an actual experiment later to test their theories but you'd like them to share how they arrived at their answers on the chart. For example, you might ask *"How did you determine how many people could stand on the raft? Sit on the raft?"* and *"Do you think we would be more comfortable sitting or standing? Why?"*

EXTENSION DURING A LATER MATH LESSON:

During math block, determine the raft's square footage and create a polygon on the floor with tape equal to the square footage. Ask the students if they want to modify their original calculations now that they see the actual dimensions. Have them test their thoughts by filling up the space of the polygon both standing and sitting.

Grade Level

5

Continuous Sum Fractions

NCTM Content Standard:

Number & Operations

NCTM Process Standard:

Communication

Specific math content or skill addressed:

Addition, fractions

Component:

Activity

Materials needed:

Deck of note cards (at least one card per student) with different fractions on each card

Preparing students for success:

Students should have experience adding fractions.

Vocabulary:

Fraction, common denominator, add

How to do it:

■ A random student begins by taking the deck and turning over the top card, revealing the fraction to the class (for example, $\frac{1}{2}$). The student then passes the deck to the student on the left.

■ The second student reveals the next card and adds that value to the previous card. For example, if the second student's card reads $\frac{3}{4}$, she should announce that the total is $1\frac{1}{4}$. She then passes the deck to the left.

■ The third student reveals a card (for example, $\frac{1}{8}$), adds the value of the card to the running total, and announces the new total ($1\frac{3}{8}$).

■ The deck continues around the circle until it is exhausted.

■ Students can execute a "lifeline" call by calling on a friend to help them if they feel stumped. Students can even pass if they would rather observe the activity.

VARIATION:

Play the game using cards with decimal amounts, instead of fractions.

Crane Problem

NCTM Content Standard:

Number & Operations

NCTM Process Standard:

Communication, Connections, Problem Solving, Representation

Specific math content or skill addressed:

Estimation, comparison

Component:

Morning message

Materials needed:

Message chart (for the morning message)

Preparing students for success:

Students should have experience with estimation and measurement.

Vocabulary:

Multiply, divide, variable, height, factor, product

How to do it:

■ Post some version of the message below. Prepare the drawing beforehand so you know the answer to your question. Consider making the man in the drawing a height that is relatively easy to convert, such as three or six inches.

■ After reading the message as a class, question the students in the following ways:

✳ *"So, how high up would you say this man was? How did you go about coming to your conclusion?"*

✳ *"If the crane hoisted the man twice as high, about how high up would he be?"*

VARIATION:

Use similar drawings to challenge the students to apply a known variable to a problem. For example, you could draw a scale model of the length of the hallway and designate a mark to represent one tile, then ask *"Knowing that each tile in the hallway has a length of one foot, how long would you estimate the hallway to be?"*

Dear Math Whizzes!!

On my way home yesterday I passed a work site where a man was hoisted up into the air by a crane. He was trimming trees. I couldn't help but wonder how high up in the air he was. I'm assuming the man is about six feet tall. I drew a sketch of the man in a bucket at the top of the crane. Considering the height of the man, how high up would you say he was based upon the drawing below?

180

Describe the Item

NCTM Content Standard:

Number & Operations,
Measurement, Geometry

NCTM Process Standard:

Communication

**Specific math content
or skill addressed:**

Mathematical description

Component:

Activity

Materials needed:

Several items familiar
to students

**Preparing students
for success:**

Students can have some
experience describing what
they see using mathematical
terminology, or this activity
can be used as an introduction
to seeing the world in this way.

Vocabulary:

There are many possibilities.

How to do it:

■ Have a collection of items concealed from the students. Possibilities include:

 ✻ Balls such as a football, baseball, basketball, or soccer ball

 ✻ Other sports-related items such as a gymnastic leotard, basketball net, or hockey stick

 ✻ Other common items like a notebook, deck of cards, stuffed animal, or laptop computer

■ Reveal the first item and offer a mathematical description. Pass the item, and ask the students to add to the oral list you have provided. Do the same with another item. For example, a basketball net could be described by saying *"It is about two feet long,"* *"It is about one foot wide,"* and *"It is sort of cone shaped."* A book could be described by saying, *"It has six sides,"* *"It has eight corners,"* and *"It has a length of twelve inches."*

■ Continue to introduce items for as long as time permits.

VARIATION:

Replay the game with different items.

EXTENSION DURING A LATER MATH LESSON:

Gather in a circle to break up a math block with some items that may be part of another curricular area (such as a map or globe for social studies).

Figure Making

How to do it:

NCTM Content Standard:
Geometry

NCTM Process Standard:
Communication,
Representation,
Reason & Proof

**Specific math content
or skill addressed:**
Identifying shapes

Component:
Morning message

Materials needed:
Clay
Message chart (for the
morning message)

**Preparing students
for success:**
Students should have
some experience with
polyhedrons.
Students should know how
to use clay in a safe and
respectful manner.

Vocabulary:
Various polyhedrons, sides,
corners, congruent

- Post some version of the message below.

Dear Builders!

Our geometry unit has introduced us to many interesting
things. I'd like you to take a few minutes before Morning
Meeting and create your own polyhedron. Study your
three-dimensional figure and prepare a statement about
it to share at the end of our meeting.

Look at my figure below on the apron of the easel. It is
a hexahedron. My statement may sound like this: "This six-
sided figure is actually a perfect hexahedron because all
the sides are congruent." Another example of what I could
say might be "I made this polyhedron in this way because
it reminds me of the box our new television came in."

Do your best and have a ball!

- After reading the message as a class, conduct an around-the-circle share
  with each student giving a statement.

- After all the statements are made, ask the students what they noticed
  about the work they all did. Possible responses include:

  ※ *"Lots of us made cubes."*

  ※ *"Tetrahedrons are hard to make."*

  ※ *"None of the people who tried making dodecahedrons finished before
  we had to come to Morning Meeting."*

Finding Area and Perimeter

NCTM Content Standard:

Number & Operations,
Geometry

NCTM Process Standard:

Communication,
Connections, Problem
Solving, Reasoning & Proof,
Representation

**Specific math content
or skill addressed:**

Geometry

Component:

Morning message

Materials needed:

Regular classroom items that
the students can measure

Note cards

Message chart (for the
morning message)

**Preparing students
for success:**

No special preparation
is required.

Vocabulary:

Add, sum, factor, product,
area, perimeter, polygon,
rectangle

How to do it:

■ Post some version of the message below.

> Dear Students,
>
> We've been exploring the relationship between area and
> perimeter over the last few days. Around our room there
> are many rectangles. Find a partner and locate at least one
> rectangle in our room. Using the metric system, measure the
> length and width of the item, then use the formulas below to
> determine the area and perimeter for the rectangle. If you
> have time, measure more than one. Write what you discover
> on a note card and bring your findings to circle for Morning
> Meeting. We'll share the information at the end of our meeting.
>
> Perimeter = 2 times length plus 2 times width (P = 2l + 2w)
>
> Area = length times width (A = l × w)

■ After reading the message as a class, have students share the perimeter
  and area of their rectangles.

■ Ask the students what they notice about the different measurements.
  You can prompt their thinking by asking:

  ✳ *"What rectangle has the largest or smallest area?"*

  ✳ *"What rectangle has the smallest or largest perimeter?"*

  ✳ *"What do you notice about the relationship between the perimeter
     and the area of the different rectangles?"*

  ✳ *"Is the area always larger than the perimeter?"*

  ✳ *"Do you think the perimeter and the area could ever be the same?"*

CONTINUED

Finding Area and Perimeter CONTINUED

- Identify two rectangles and ask the students to estimate the total area and perimeter of these rectangles. Then pick one and see if the students can estimate what half the area and perimeter of the one rectangle would be.

- Challenge the students to think about what the area would be if all the rectangles were laid down next to one another. Also ask them to think about what the total perimeter of a large polygon made of all their rectangles would be. The lead-in might sound like *"What would be the area and perimeter of a polygon that was made up of all our rectangles laid side by side?"*

VARIATION:

Repeat this message with a focus on polyhedrons.

EXTENSIONS DURING A LATER MATH LESSON:

- Have each pair of students recreate the dimensions of the rectangle they measured by cutting it out of a piece of paper.

- Create a massive polygon and examine it as a group.

Flip Card Game

How to do it:

■ Distribute three cards face down to each member of the circle.

■ The student two from your right flips over a card. Announce the number that has been revealed. Then have the student immediately to your right flip one of his or her cards. Announce that number too. Then declare a relationship that these two numbers have. For example, if the first card is 8.2 and the second card is 5, you could announce *"8.2 is 3.2 greater than 5."* Other examples might be: *"8.2 is about 3 greater than 5," "8.2 is greater than 5,"* or *"5 is less than 8.2."* Stress that any true statement can be used and that students can call for a lifeline with the child to their right if they feel they need to.

■ Explain that since you declared the relationship, you are now the person who flips over a card. The person immediately to your left then reveals a card. The person two to your left now declares the relationship between the two revealed numbers.

■ The flow of the game continues. After the cards have been exhausted they can be quickly shuffled for another round, if time permits.

VARIATIONS:

■ Once the students are good at this game, increase the difficulty by inserting more mixed numbers or larger numbers.

■ Create a deck of money amounts or percentages.

EXTENSION DURING A LATER MATH LESSON:

To break up a math block, gather in a circle and play a quick round.

Grab and Attribute

NCTM Content Standard:

Geometry

NCTM Process Standard:

Communication,
Representation

**Specific math content
or skill addressed:**

Identifying shapes,
attribution

Component:

Activity

Materials needed:

Variety of objects small
enough to fit in a brown
paper bag that correspond
to various geometric shapes
(see example chart for ideas).
You can also use gaming dice
for more advanced shapes.

Brown paper bags

**Preparing students
for success:**

Students should have
experience working with
three-dimensional figures and
communicating attributes.

Vocabulary:

Various polyhedrons,
sides, angles, corners,
area, perimeter

How to do it:

■ Fill a couple of bags with enough items for each child to have one.

■ Pass the bags around the circle, having the students pick one item.

■ Model for the group how you may describe the item you have picked. You may say something like *"This is a hexahedron. The area on this side is about twelve square inches"* or *"My guess is that some of the sides are about three inches long and others are about four inches long."* Encourage the students to use mathematical words.

■ Ask for volunteers to describe their items.

EXTENSION DURING A LATER MATH LESSON:

Have the students bring in polyhedrons they may have at home and share them.

Cone	Cube	Cylinder	Sphere	Rectangular Prism
Spinning tops	Blocks	Lipstick tube	Balls	Eraser
Play ice-cream cone	Dice	Cans	Hackey sacks	Tissue box
Paper cone cup	Rubik's cube	Kaleidoscopes	Marbles	Book
Party hats	Note cubes	Marshmallows	Oranges	
Cake decorating tips		Pencil holder	Small globe	
		Toilet paper rolls		

Group Memory

NCTM Content Standard:

Number & Operations

NCTM Process Standard:

Connections

**Specific math content
or skill addressed:**

Addition, subtraction,
multiplication, division,
estimation

Component:

Activity

Materials needed:

A deck of cards with numbers
that create equations

**Preparing students
for success:**

Students need experience
with whichever operations
will be practiced.

Students need to be quiet
and respectful when it is not
their turn to flip a card.

Vocabulary:

Depending upon the
operation, there are
many possibilities.

How to do it:

■ To save time, have the cards already face down when the students come to circle. The cards should reflect what you are currently working on in math class—for example, if you want to focus on multiplication, use cards like 7, 8, 56, 9, 9, 81, 11, 11, 121, 12, 12, and 144.

■ Explain that the group will take turns flipping one card at a time by entering the circle. They'll be counting on their memories and mathematical skills to eventually eliminate all the cards.

■ Begin the game. If the operation is multiplication, it may proceed like this:

❋ The first student enters the circle and flips a 9.

❋ The second student then flips 81.

❋ The third student will be looking for where the other 9 is. If no match is found, then the cards are returned to their face down position and the class does the best they can to remember where the previously flipped numbers are located. If a match is found, the matching cards are removed from the display.

■ The game continues until all matches are found.

VARIATION:

Once students understand the game, increase the difficulty by introducing mixed numbers and varying operations.

EXTENSIONS DURING A LATER MATH LESSON:

■ Gather in a circle and play this game to break up a math block.

■ Provide several decks and have students play in smaller groups. (This may even be a good way to introduce the game.)

Matching and Drawing

NCTM Content Standard:

Number & Operations

NCTM Process Standard:

Communication,
Representation

**Specific math content
or skill addressed:**

Fractions, decimals,
comparison

Component:

Activity

Materials needed:

Pencils

A deck of 5 × 8 note cards
for drawing on

A deck of 3 × 5 note cards
that contains matching cards
with decimals and fractions

**Preparing students
for success:**

Students should have
experience working with
both fractions and decimals.

Vocabulary:

Fraction, decimal,
representation, amount

How to do it:

■ Give each student a note card with a fraction or a decimal. Cards may include the following (or similar pairs):

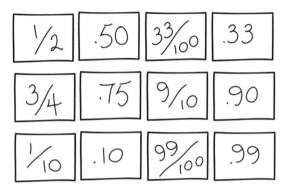

■ They must find the person in the class who has a card that matches theirs. Once they find their matching partner, the two of them draw a picture that represents their number on a 5 × 8 note card. After they finish drawing, they find seats in the circle next to one another—this is the signal that they are finished.

■ Once all the students are seated, ask for volunteers to share how they figured out whether a classmate's number matches theirs. Volunteers also share their drawings.

■ Collect the cards, shuffle them, and redistribute them for another round if there is time.

VARIATION:

Increase the difficulty by altering the deck. Eventually bring in mixed numbers.

EXTENSION DURING A LATER MATH LESSON:

Have the students write story problems using the fractions/decimals used in the activity.

Mixed Number Making

NCTM Content Standard:

Number & Operations,
Data Analysis & Probability

NCTM Process Standard:

Communication, Reasoning
& Proof, Representation

**Specific math content
or skill addressed:**

Counting, place value

Component:

Activity

Materials needed:

Note cards

**Preparing students
for success:**

Students should be
comfortable with mixed
numbers.

Vocabulary:

Mixed number, fraction,
least, greatest, range

How to do it:

■ The day before you do the activity, provide students with a homework assignment that reads like the following:

> Everyone has worked hard at learning how to work with mixed numbers. Tomorrow at Morning Meeting, we're going to do some activities using mixed numbers. It is up to you to create a drawing that represents a mixed number on one side of a note card. Write the mixed number on the other side. You must choose a mixed number that is greater than 2 and less than 10. Here is an example of what each side of the card may look like:

> Tomorrow at Morning Meeting, bring your card to circle and place it behind you until it's time for the activity.

■ At the next day's Morning Meeting, have all the students show the picture representations of their mixed numbers one at a time going around the circle. As a group, the students try to assign the correct value to each of the pictures.

■ Ask for someone to identify the highest and lowest mixed numbers, and see if a volunteer can explain the range of the numbers.

■ If time permits, have students sit with their cards and call for pop-ups based on a certain criteria. For example, you may say *"If your mixed number is within ¾ of four, pop up."* All the students within that range pop up. Have them sit back down and announce other criteria such as *"If your number is between five and eight, pop up."* Examine the mixed numbers the students have created and create a variety of criteria.

CONTINUED

Mixed Number Making

EXTENSIONS DURING A LATER MATH LESSON:

- Line up the cards in order, from least to greatest.

- Challenge the students later in math class to see if they can determine the actual sum of all the mixed numbers. Share what strategies are used. Possible strategies reported might be:

  ✳ *"I estimated based on the whole number the mixed number was closest to, then I added the whole numbers together."*

  ✳ *"I went down the line and added them one after the other."*

  ✳ *"I took the greatest and the least amounts and added them, then estimated the rest."*

Name Values Multiplication

NCTM Content Standard:
Number & Operations

NCTM Process Standard:
Problem Solving

**Specific math content
or skill addressed:**
Multiplication

Component:
Morning message

Materials needed:
Chart of letter values
Scrap paper and pencils
Message chart (for the
morning message)

**Preparing students
for success:**
Students should have some
experience with adding
strings of numbers and know
some strategies for doing so.

Vocabulary:
Value, factor, product,
chart, variable

How to do it:

- Prepare a chart like the one at the right that gives values to letters of the alphabet.

- On the morning message, include the following related task:

  Use the letter value chart to figure out how many points you would get for each letter of your name. Then, find the product of the letters of your first name. Write your name and your total in the space below.

- During the message portion of the meeting, reflect with students on the results by asking some of these questions:

  ❋ *"Whose name has the least number of points?"*

  ❋ *"Whose name has the most points? So, the range of our names goes from ___ to ___."*

  ❋ *"Whose names are equal in value?"*

  ❋ *"If we were going to add up all of our names together, how many points do you think we would have? How could we find out?"*

A = 1	N = 1
B = 3	O = 1
C = 3	P = 3
D = 2	Q = 10
E = 1	R = 1
F = 4	S = 1
G = 2	T = 1
H = 4	U = 1
I = 1	V = 4
J = 8	W = 4
K = 5	X = 8
L = 1	Y = 4
M = 3	Z = 10

Example: CAT $3 \times 1 \times 1 = 3$

VARIATIONS:

- Repeat for middle names, last names, etc.

- In the message ask students to choose a word (from the word wall, dictionary, a unit of study, etc.) and calculate the total for that word.

- Use different letter values: five points for consonants, ten for vowels, or a coin value for each letter, etc.

EXTENSIONS DURING A LATER MATH LESSON:

- Challenge the students to figure out the product of various math words they're working with.

- Ask students *"If you could change one letter in your name, which letter would you change and why? What would your new name and value be?"* Let students share their responses.

- As a class or individually, have students graph the results from the message.

Our Metric Heights

NCTM Content Standard:
Number & Operations

NCTM Process Standard:
Communication, Connections, Reasoning & Proof

Specific math content or skill addressed:
Measurement

Component:
Morning message, activity

Materials needed:
Meter sticks

Note cards

Message chart (for the morning message)

Preparing students for success:
Students should have experience measuring items with a meter stick and expressing amounts using decimals.

Vocabulary:
Whole, tenths, hundredths, meters, decimeters, centimeters

How to do it:

■ Post some version of the message below.

> Dear Mathematicians,
>
> You have grown. Really, you have. You're not even close to being the height you all were at the beginning of the year. So, here's your challenge!
>
> Consider what you have been learning in our work with decimals and what you already know about the metric system. For now, write down on a note card an estimate of your metric height using decimals and bring it to Morning Meeting. We'll be working in pairs to find our actual metric heights as an activity.
>
> I estimated that my metric height is 1.65 meters. That means that I would say I'm one whole meter plus six decimeters and 5 centimeters. A math sentence of this compilation of numbers would look like this: $1 + .6 + .05 = 1.65$.

■ During activity time, pair up the students so that there is one meter stick for every two students. Each student will measure the other.

■ Working together, they record their metric heights in decimal form.

■ Conduct a discussion asking the students to express what they discovered through their work together. Ask them *"What did you find in your work together?"* Possible responses might be:

　✷ *"I was exactly a quarter of a meter taller than my partner."*

　✷ *"We are all pretty close to being around a meter and a half tall."*

■ Also ask *"How does using the decimals work with the metric system?"* and *"Do you think it would be difficult to use decimals if you were using U.S. standard measurement?"*

EXTENSION DURING A LATER MATH LESSON:

Have the students determine the total height of the class by adding all the heights together. Express the sum in decimal form.

Scaling Floor Layouts

NCTM Content Standard:

Geometry, Measurement

NCTM Process Standard:

Connections, Representation

Specific math content or skill addressed:

Measurement

Component:

Sharing

Materials needed:

Graph paper

Ruler

Pencil

Bedroom

Preparing students for success:

Students should have a working knowledge of scale drawing. Modeling the activity by measuring off the classroom itself could serve as a beginning.

Vocabulary:

Scale, measure, centimeter, inch, foot, feet, ruler

How to do it:

■ A week before the sharing, provide students with a homework assignment that reads like the following:

> This week you'll be challenged to create a scale drawing of your bedroom using the graph paper you've been issued. You'll be drawing a layout for your bedroom as we did of the classroom.
>
> Each square on your graph paper will represent six square inches. That means that four squares are equal to one square foot. Follow the step-by-step instructions for nightly work to have your scale drawing ready for the end of the week.
>
> ### Monday
>
> Measure the outline of your bedroom. Draw the outline of your bedroom on the graph paper using a ruler. Remember, each line of a square is equal to six inches.
>
> ### Tuesday
>
> Measure the furniture in your bedroom. Create a list of the items with their lengths and widths. You may want to begin with your bed. Other items may include a dresser, chest, desk, or nightstand.
>
> ### Wednesday
>
> Within your bedroom layout draw in the items you measured last night. Label the items accordingly like we did with the classroom drawing.
>
> ### Thursday
>
> Put any needed final touches on your drawing. Use color to designate different items like we did for our classroom. Prepare to tell us about your bedroom and the things in it. Also, be prepared to share a thought or two about how you might rearrange your bedroom and how it might appear on your drawing.

■ Students share their work with the class, over a number of days if necessary.

CONTINUED

Scaling Floor Layouts

VARIATION:

Instead of assigning homework, give students or teams of students the task of measuring rooms within the school or parts of the classroom. Keep a master grid on graph paper that each student or team can update to create a complete picture of the school or classroom.

EXTENSIONS DURING A LATER MATH LESSON:

■ This assignment can be repeated using another room.

■ Have students calculate the area and perimeter of their room.

Shooting Percentages

NCTM Content Standard:

Data Analysis & Probability,
Number & Operations

NCTM Process Standard:

Problem Solving

**Specific math content
or skill addressed:**

Data analysis

Component:

Morning message

Materials needed:

Calculators

Message chart (for the
morning message)

**Preparing students
for success:**

Students should have
experience with examining
data and calculating
percentages.

Vocabulary:

Data, average, divide,
dividend, quotient,
divisor, about

How to do it:

■ Post some version of the message below.

> Dear Students!
>
> The high school team had a big win the other night. Three of the players on our team went to this school. Examine the statistics of their shooting last Friday night. First, predict who you think had the highest and lowest percentage by simply looking at the numbers. Then, with a classmate, calculate their shooting percentages. Bring your findings with you to Morning Meeting.
>
> | Name | Shots Taken | Shots Made |
> | --- | --- | --- |
> | Kate Amelo | 8 | 2 |
> | Tisha Jones | 10 | 3 |
> | Karen Lewis | 14 | 4 |

■ After reading the message as a class, ask for volunteers to share their answers. Redo the calculations in front of the group to verify their calculations.

EXTENSION DURING A LATER MATH LESSON:

Follow the players throughout the season and keep a running shooting percentage.

Snowman Message

NCTM Content Standard:

Geometry, Number &
Operations, Measurement

NCTM Process Standard:

Connections, Representation

**Specific math content
or skill addressed:**

Measurement, prediction,
data analysis

Component:

Morning message

Materials needed:

Message chart (for the
morning message)

**Preparing students
for success:**

Students should have
some experience with
measurement and scale.

Vocabulary:

Inch, foot, scale, size,
measure, estimate

How to do it:

■ Post some version of the message below.

Dear Winter Wonderers!

It's winter! Do you know the song "Winter Wonderland," and how the kids in that song made a snowman? I have drawn a scale model of a snowman below. Every foot is represented by 2 inches. With a friend, use your math skills to determine the actual size of the snowman.

Here's a brainteaser for you! If the weather gets warmer, make a guess at how many days it will take for the snowman to melt to half its size.

How about ¼ its size?

Gone completely?

■ After reading the message as a class, ask volunteers to share their answer to the size of the snowman problem and how they arrived at it.

■ Ask students to share their answers to the various brainteaser problems and how they went about solving the problems.

EXTENSION DURING A LATER MATH LESSON:

Have students make scale drawings of snowmen they have created or would like to create.

Toss and Call with Numbers

NCTM Content Standard:

Number & Operations

NCTM Process Standard:

Problem Solving,
Communication

**Specific math content
or skill addressed:**

Addition, subtraction,
multiplication, division,
estimation, number
relationships

Component:

Activity

Materials needed:

A beach ball with numbers
written on or taped to
each section

**Preparing students
for success:**

Students need experience
with computations.

Vocabulary:

About, greater than,
less than, equals, and
all the operations

How to do it:

■ Begin by modeling how to toss and catch the beach ball. When you catch the ball, model how one hand will land on one section of the ball and another hand will land on another section. Explain that this is important because each section has a different number.

■ Bring attention to the numbers that are in the sections where your hands are. For instance, if your left hand is in the section with the number 12 in it and your right hand is in the section with the number 15 in it, call out the two numbers, then ask *"What do we know about these two numbers?"* After a few seconds of wait time, members of the circle call out answers. Responses might be:

✻ *"Twelve is three less than fifteen."*

✻ *"Fifteen is three more than twelve."*

✻ *"Twelve plus fifteen is twenty-seven."*

✻ *"Twelve times fifteen is greater than 150."*

✻ *"$^{12}/_{15}$ is $^4/_5$."*

✻ *"$^{15}/_{12}$ is greater than a whole."*

■ Gently toss the ball to a student and continue the process. The student catches the beach ball, identifies the numbers, and announces *"What do we know about __ and __ ?"*

■ Repeat the process until the class has explored many combinations of numbers and their relationships.

EXTENSIONS DURING A LATER MATH LESSON:

■ Change the numbers by having different numbers ready to be taped to the ball during the game.

■ Play this game in the middle of a math block to get the students out of their seats and moving.

Toss and Call with Operations

NCTM Content Standard:

Number & Operations

NCTM Process Standard:

Problem Solving,
Communications

**Specific math content
or skill addressed:**

Addition, subtraction,
multiplication, division,
estimation, mental math

Component:

Activity

Materials needed:

A beach ball with different
operations written on or
taped to each section

**Preparing students
for success:**

Students need experience
with whichever operations
are written on the beach ball.

Vocabulary:

All operations, equals

How to do it:

- Begin by modeling how to toss and catch the beach ball. When you catch the ball, explain that the operation your left hand lands on is the operation with which you'll be working.

- Bring attention to the operation. For instance, if your left hand was in the section with the operation subtraction, call out *"Subtraction"* and announce two numbers. The students consider the difference between the two numbers. After a few seconds of wait time, call on a student who believes she knows the answer.

- Gently toss the ball to a student and continue the process. The student catches the beach ball, identifies the operation, and then announces two numbers.

- Calls from students after catching the beach ball may sound like:

    "Multiplication, two and 221."
    "Addition, 78½ and six."
    "Division, 400 and three."

- Be sure to stress the importance of wait time so that all students have a chance to be heard.

- Make sure everyone has a chance to catch and toss the ball.

VARIATION:

Provide a chart listing numbers that are to be used in the game, emphasizing numbers related to the current math lesson. For example, if the group is focusing on fractions or decimals, then numbers with fractions and decimals can be listed on the chart.

The Wall Message

NCTM Content Standard:

Data Analysis & Probability, Number & Operations, Measurement

NCTM Process Standard:

Reasoning & Proof

Specific math content or skill addressed:

Measurement, prediction, data analysis, counting

Component:

Morning message

Materials needed:

Message chart (for the morning message)

Preparing students for success:

Students should have experience with estimation.

Following these directions might take awhile, so this activity works best if students are in the classroom well before Morning Meeting.

Vocabulary:

Area, leverage, estimation

How to do it:

■ Post some version of the message below.

> Dear Adventurers,
>
> I took a walk this past weekend and came across a wall attached to an old building. It was 100 feet long and 3 feet tall. All the cinder blocks were about the same size. I wondered how many cinder blocks it took to make that wall. I counted 20 cinder blocks over a 5-foot stretch of the wall. About how many cinder blocks do you think the 100-foot wall was made with? Work with a friend before coming to Morning Meeting to come up with an estimate. Use any tools in our room that may help you. We'll discuss this investigation at the end of Morning Meeting.

■ After reading the message as a class, ask for volunteers to share their answers. List the answers on the message chart. Ask students what they notice about the different estimates. Ask specifics such as *"Are the estimates close to one another or far apart?"* and *"What numbers appear most often?"*

■ Have students share how they went about arriving at their estimates and what was most challenging about this problem.

EXTENSION DURING A LATER MATH LESSON:

For homework, ask students to find a wall and determine how many bricks or stones it took to make it.

199

What Would Cover It?

NCTM Content Standard:
Geometry, Measurement

NCTM Process Standard:
Communication, Representation

Specific math content or skill addressed:
Measurement

Component:
Activity

Materials needed:
Color tiles (one inch square)

Shoe box

Chart

Preparing students for success:
Students should have experience working with three-dimensional figures and determining surface area.

Vocabulary:
Surface area, square inches, measurement, multiply, add

How to do it:

- Tell the students they'll be estimating the surface area of a shoe box, and as a group they'll be testing their thinking using one-square-inch color tiles.

- Place the shoe box in the middle of the circle with the largest surface area at the top. Have the students around the circle share what they believe the total surface of the shoe box is using square inches.

- Record their estimates on a chart.

- Once all the students have made their estimates, place several bags of color tiles around the circle. Begin by having one student place a limited number of color tiles, perhaps five, on the top surface.

- Ask the students if any of them would like to change their estimates. If so, revise the chart or add their new estimates to a different area on the chart.

- Continue around the circle adding color tiles. At various points revisit their estimates for the surface area of the entire shoe box.

- Once the surface area of one side has been determined, ask them if they need to go through the process again for the opposing surface area. (Students should answer no. Multiplying the largest surface area by two will give them the total surface area of the two largest sides.)

- Remove the color tiles and turn the shoe box so that the smallest surface area is now on the top.

- Repeat the process explained above, stopping at points to see if any of the students want to revisit their estimations.

- Once the smallest surface area has been determined, ask them if they need to determine the measurement for the opposing side. (Students should answer no. Multiplying the smallest surface area by two will give them the total surface area of the two smallest sides.)

- Remove the color tiles and turn the shoe box so that one of the last surface areas is now on the top.

- Repeat the process explained above, stopping at points to see if any of the students want to revisit their estimations.

- Once this surface area has been determined, ask them if they need to determine the measurement for the opposing side. (Students should answer no. Multiplying the last surface area measured by two will give them the total surface area of the last two sides.)

- Calculate the total surface area of the shoe box with the class.

- If time permits, introduce another size shoe box and repeat the process.

VARIATION:

Use a box that has more than two equally-sized sides.

EXTENSIONS DURING A LATER MATH LESSON:

- Have the students bring in a variety of shoe boxes that each can estimate the surface area for and test.

- After students have worked through this challenge, use asymmetrical figures.

What's Our Sum Decimals

NCTM Content Standard:

Number & Operations

NCTM Process Standard:

Communication

Specific math content or skill addressed:

Decimals, addition, mental math

Component:

Activity

Materials needed:

Note cards with a range of decimals written on them

Preparing students for success:

Students should have experience with adding decimals.

Vocabulary:

Addend, sum, decimal, mixed number

How to do it:

■ Introduce the activity to the students as a group practice of the skills they've been working on. Remind students how to treat others who may not know the answer or call out an incorrect answer.

■ Each student is given a card with a mixed number such as 2.5, 3.75, or 4.25.

■ Choose two students at random and ask the circle *"What is the sum of Danielle and Diamond?"*

■ Danielle announces her number (for example, 2.5); then Diamond announces her number (for example, 3.75).

■ Wait five seconds, and then ask *"The sum is?"* The students call out the answer in unison (6.25).

VARIATIONS:

■ Increase the challenge by going beyond the tenths place, using hundredths and thousandths.

■ Play What's Our Difference Decimals by subtracting the decimals, rather than adding them.

What's Our Sum Fractions

NCTM Content Standard:

Number & Operations

NCTM Process Standard:

Communication

Specific math content or skill addressed:

Fractions, addition, mental math

Component:

Activity

Materials needed:

Note cards with a range of fractions written on them

Preparing students for success:

Students should have experience with adding fractions.

Vocabulary:

Addend, sum, fraction, mixed number

How to do it:

■ Introduce the activity to the students as a group practice of the skills they've been working on. Remind students how to treat others who may not know the answer or call out an incorrect answer.

■ Each student is given a card with a mixed number such as $2\frac{1}{2}$, $3\frac{3}{4}$, or $4\frac{1}{4}$.

■ Choose two students at random and ask the circle *"What is the sum of Aiden and Sumi?"*

■ Aiden announces his number (for example, $2\frac{1}{2}$); then Sumi announces her number (for example, $3\frac{3}{4}$).

■ Wait five seconds, and then ask *"The sum is?"* The students call out the answer in unison ($6\frac{1}{4}$).

VARIATIONS:

■ Increase the challenge by having the students work with fractions other than halves and fourths so they have to find a common denominator in their head.

■ Play What's Our Difference Fractions by subtracting the fractions, rather than adding them.

Which One Doesn't Belong?

NCTM Content Standard:

Number & Operations,
Algebra

NCTM Process Standard:

Reasoning, Communication

**Specific math content
or skill addressed:**

Number relationships

Component:

Morning message

Materials needed:

Message chart (for the
morning message)

**Preparing students
for success:**

Students should be
experienced at analyzing
numbers.

Vocabulary:

Digit, odd/even

How to do it:

■ Include some version of the following as a related task on the morning message:

Be thinking about which one of these numbers does not belong: 9, 16, 36, 60, 66

■ During the message portion of the meeting, ask students which number they think does not belong and why. Encourage students to think of many possible answers. Possible responses include:

✳ *"The nine because it has only one digit and the others have two."*

✳ *"The nine because it is odd, and the others are even."*

✳ *"Sixteen because if you counted by threes, you would hit all of the other numbers but not the sixteen."*

✳ *"66 because it has two of the same digits, and the others do not."*

Activity Subject Lists

Grade Level

K

		GREETING	SHARING	GROUP ACTIVITY	MORNING MESSAGE
ADDITION	Plus/Minus, p. 29			✓	
ALGEBRA	Yes/No Questions, p. 39				✓
ATTRIBUTION	Attribute Train, p. 14			✓	
	So Does Mine, p. 33			✓	
COMPARISON	Faster, Lower, Higher, p. 18			✓	
	Shorter/Longer, p. 31				✓
	Yes/No Questions, p. 39				✓
COUNTING	Beats in a Name, p. 15			✓	
	Collections Sharing, p. 16		✓		
	Dance with Me, p. 17			✓	
	Number Lineup, p. 24			✓	
	Number Line Walk, p. 25			✓	
	Shoe Graph, p. 30			✓	
	Shorter/Longer, p. 31				✓
	Skip Greeting, p. 32	✓			
	Under the Cup, p. 38			✓	
	Yes/No Questions, p. 39				✓
DATA ANALYSIS	All Grown Up, p. 13		✓		✓
GRAPHS & DIAGRAMS	Shoe Graph, p. 30			✓	
IDENTIFYING NUMBERS	Fiddle Faddle, p. 19			✓	
	Number Lineup, p. 24			✓	
	Numbers in My House, p. 26		✓		
IDENTIFYING SHAPES	I Spy a Shape, p. 22			✓	
	Lines, Lines Everywhere, p. 23				✓
	String Shapes, p. 35			✓	

Grade Level
K

		GREETING	SHARING	GROUP ACTIVITY	MORNING MESSAGE
LINE SEGMENTS	Lines, Lines Everywhere, p. 23				✓
MATHEMATICAL DESCRIPTION	Zero Sharing, p. 41		✓		
MEASUREMENT	Dance with Me, p. 17			✓	
	Shorter/Longer, p. 31				✓
MONEY	So Does Mine, p. 33			✓	
NAVIGATIONAL DIRECTIONS	Dance with Me, p. 17			✓	
NUMBER RELATIONSHIPS	All Grown Up, p. 13		✓		✓
	Fiddle Faddle, p. 19			✓	
	Number Line Walk, p. 25			✓	
	Numbers in My House, p. 26		✓		
	Skip Greeting, p. 32	✓			
	Under the Cup, p. 38			✓	
ODD & EVEN	Odd or Even, p. 27			✓	
PART/WHOLE RELATIONSHIPS	Beats in a Name, p. 15			✓	
PATTERNS	Growing Pattern Songs, p. 20			✓	
	Patterns Around the Circle, p. 28			✓	
SORTING/ GROUPING	Collections Sharing, p. 16		✓		
	So Does Mine, p. 33			✓	
SUBTRACTION	Plus/Minus, p. 29			✓	
TIME	Time to . . . , p. 37			✓	

207

		GREETING	SHARING	GROUP ACTIVITY	MORNING MESSAGE
ADDITION	Adding Our Way to 100, p. 43			✓	
	Beanbag Toss, p. 45			✓	
	How Many to Ten?, p. 52			✓	
	Magic Doubles, p. 56			✓	
	Start with Ten, p. 69			✓	
	Tiles in a Bag, p. 71				✓
CHARTS	Beanbag Toss, p. 45			✓	
COMPARISON	Scoop 'Em Up, p. 64				✓
	Seconds, Minutes, Hours, p. 66			✓	
COUNTING	Adding Our Way to 100, p. 43			✓	
	Card Greeting, p. 46	✓			
	A Clip and Save Meeting, p. 48	✓	✓	✓	✓
	Dice Greeting, p. 50	✓			
	How Many to Ten?, p. 52			✓	
	Measuring in Tens and Ones, p. 60			✓	✓
	Number Grid Puzzle, p. 61			✓	
	Quarters, p. 63			✓	
	Scoop 'Em Up, p. 64				✓
	Seconds, Minutes, Hours, p. 66			✓	
DATA ANALYSIS	Beanbag Toss, p. 45			✓	
	Class Detectives, p. 47			✓	✓
	Favorites Graph, p. 51				✓
FRACTIONS	A Trail Mix Recipe, p. 72				✓
GRAPHS & DIAGRAMS	Favorites Graph, p. 51				✓
IDENTIFYING NUMBERS	Magic Doubles, p. 56			✓	

		GREETING	SHARING	GROUP ACTIVITY	MORNING MESSAGE
IDENTIFYING SHAPES	Make a Shape, p. 58			✓	
	Shape Hunt, p. 68		✓		✓
MEASUREMENT	How Much Space?, p. 53				✓
	If I Were One Inch Tall, p. 55		✓		✓
	Measuring in Tens and Ones, p. 60			✓	✓
	A Trail Mix Recipe, p. 72				✓
MONEY	A Clip and Save Meeting, p. 48	✓	✓	✓	✓
	Quarters, p. 63			✓	
NUMBER RELATIONSHIPS	Card Greeting, p. 46	✓			
	Dice Greeting, p. 50	✓			
	Hundreds Chart Paths, p. 54			✓	
	Number Grid Puzzle, p. 61			✓	
	Two Is King, p. 73			✓	
PART/WHOLE RELATIONSHIPS	Make a Shape, p. 58			✓	
PATTERNS	Pattern of the Day, p. 62			✓	
	Two Is King, p. 73			✓	
PLACE VALUE	Hundreds Chart Paths, p. 54			✓	
	Number Grid Puzzle, p. 61			✓	
SORTING/ GROUPING	Measuring in Tens and Ones, p. 60			✓	✓
	This Group, That Group, p. 70			✓	
SUBTRACTION	Start with Ten, p. 69			✓	
TIME	Seconds, Minutes, Hours, p. 66			✓	

Grade Level

2

		GREETING	SHARING	GROUP ACTIVITY	MORNING MESSAGE
ADDITION	Broken Calculator, p. 78				✓
	Card Combination Game, p. 79			✓	
	Catch the Bug, p. 80			✓	
	Magic 20, p. 90			✓	
	Name Values, p. 97				✓
	Six Rolls to 100, p. 100			✓	
	Skip Greeting with Cards, p. 102	✓			
	What Number Am I?, p. 107			✓	
ALGEBRA	Broken Calculator, p. 78				✓
	Catch the Bug, p. 80			✓	
	Magic 20, p. 90			✓	
	What Number Am I?, p. 107			✓	
ATTRIBUTION	Guess *Your* Number, p. 85			✓	
COUNTING	Money for Nothin', p. 95			✓	
DATA ANALYSIS	Bouncing Balls, p. 76				✓
	Graphing Pockets, p. 82				✓
	Spinners, p. 103				✓
	Venn Diagrams, p. 104				✓
ESTIMATION	Guess *Your* Number, p. 85			✓	
	Guess *Your* Shape, p. 86			✓	
GRAPHS & DIAGRAMS	Bouncing Balls, p. 76				✓
	Give It Time, p. 81				✓
	Graphing Pockets, p. 82				✓
	Venn Diagrams, p. 104				✓
IDENTIFYING NUMBERS	Card Combination Game, p. 79			✓	

210

		GREETING	SHARING	GROUP ACTIVITY	MORNING MESSAGE
IDENTIFYING SHAPES	Are You a Rectangle?, p. 75				✓
	Guess *Your* Shape, p. 86			✓	
	Human Polygons, p. 87			✓	
	It Could Be a . . . , p. 89		✓		
MATHEMATICAL DESCRIPTION	Guess *Your* Number, p. 85			✓	
	Guess *Your* Shape, p. 86			✓	
MEASUREMENT	Are You a Rectangle?, p. 75				✓
	Measure Yourself, p. 94				✓
MENTAL MATH	Guess My Number, p. 84			✓	
	Six Rolls to 100, p. 100			✓	
MONEY	Money for Nothin', p. 95			✓	
MULTIPLICATION	Card Combination Game, p. 79			✓	
ODD & EVEN	Card Combination Game, p. 79			✓	
PATTERNS	Name Patterns, p. 96			✓	
PLACE VALUE	Make the Number, p. 91			✓	
	Roll a Big One, p. 98			✓	
	Six Rolls to 100, p. 100			✓	
PREDICTION	Give It Time, p. 81				✓
SUBTRACTION	Broken Calculator, p. 78				✓
	Catch the Bug, p. 80			✓	

Grade Level
3

	GREETING	SHARING	GROUP ACTIVITY	MORNING MESSAGE
ADDITION Base Ten Block Building, p. 109			✓	
Beach Ball Tossing, p. 110			✓	
Double This, p. 118			✓	
How Much Money?, p. 123			✓	
Magical Mystery Machine, p. 125			✓	
Make Ten, p. 126	✓		✓	
COMPARISON Body Math, p. 111			✓	
COUNTING Digit Pop, p. 115			✓	
Tens, p. 139			✓	
DATA ANALYSIS Coin Flip Probability, p. 114			✓	
Marble Probability, p. 127			✓	
Spinner Probability, p. 137			✓	
DIVISION Magical Mystery Machine, p. 125			✓	
ESTIMATION Examining Temperatures, p. 120				✓
How Much Money?, p. 123			✓	
Piloting, p. 134			✓	
Tens, p. 139			✓	
GRAPHS & DIAGRAMS Examining Temperatures, p. 120				✓
IDENTIFYING NUMBERS Base Ten Block Building, p. 109			✓	
Beach Ball Tossing, p. 110			✓	
IDENTIFYING SHAPES Isosceles Triangle Message, p. 124				✓
Ruler Around the Room, p. 135		✓		✓
MATHEMATICAL DESCRIPTION Equations and Pictures, p. 119				✓

		GREETING	SHARING	GROUP ACTIVITY	MORNING MESSAGE
MEASUREMENT	Body Math, p. 111			✓	
	Dimensions in the Bubble, p. 116				✓
	Piloting, p. 134			✓	
	Ruler Around the Room, p. 135		✓		✓
MENTAL MATH	Body Math, p. 111			✓	
	Mental Math Pushups, p. 128			✓	
MONEY	How Much Money?, p. 123			✓	
MULTIPLICATION	Base Ten Block Building, p. 109			✓	
	Beach Ball Tossing, p. 110			✓	
	Double This, p. 118			✓	
	Magical Mystery Machine, p. 125			✓	
	Multiplying Us, p. 131			✓	
	Things in Groups #1, p. 140				✓
NAVIGATIONAL DIRECTIONS	Piloting, p. 134			✓	
NUMBER RELATIONSHIPS	Message Relationships, p. 129				✓
	Pica Ferme Nada, p. 132			✓	
PREDICTION	Coin Flip Probability, p. 114			✓	
	Examining Temperatures, p. 120				✓
	Marble Probability, p. 127			✓	
	Spinner Probability, p. 137			✓	
PROBABILITY	Coin Flip Probability, p. 114			✓	
	Marble Probability, p. 127			✓	
	Spinner Probability, p. 137			✓	

CONTINUED

Grade Level

3

CONTINUED

		GREETING	SHARING	GROUP ACTIVITY	MORNING MESSAGE
SORTING/ GROUPING	Base Ten Block Building, p. 109			✓	
	Beach Ball Tossing, p. 110			✓	
	Multiplying Us, p. 131			✓	
SUBTRACTION	Base Ten Block Building, p. 109			✓	
	Beach Ball Tossing, p. 110			✓	
	Magical Mystery Machine, p. 125			✓	
TIME	Clock Check-In, p. 112				✓
	How Long Will It Bounce?, p. 122				✓

		GREETING	SHARING	GROUP ACTIVITY	MORNING MESSAGE
ADDITION	Algebra Card Game, p. 143			✓	
	Battery Algebra, p. 149				✓
	How Many Ways, p. 158				✓
	Match Card Greeting, p. 164	✓			
	Pass the Deck Operations, p. 166			✓	
	Sharing Milk, p. 168				✓
ALGEBRA	Algebra Card Game, p. 143			✓	
	Battery Algebra, p. 149				✓
ATTRIBUTION	Attribution Messages, p. 144				✓
CHARTS	Coded Messages, p. 150				✓
	Estimating and Measuring, p. 153				✓
	How Tall Would We Be?, p. 159			✓	
COUNTING	Bacon and Eggs, p. 146			✓	
	Coin Combinations, p. 151				✓
DATA ANALYSIS	Attribution Messages, p. 144				✓
	How Do We Relate?, p. 157			✓	
DIVISION	Algebra Card Game, p. 143			✓	
	Bacon and Eggs, p. 146			✓	
	How Many Ways, p. 158				✓
	Match Card Greeting, p. 164	✓			
	Pass the Deck Operations, p. 166			✓	
	Split the Group, p. 171			✓	
	Split Up the Bags, p. 172			✓	

CONTINUED

		GREETING	SHARING	GROUP ACTIVITY	MORNING MESSAGE
ESTIMATION	Estimate the Amount, p. 152			✓	
	Estimating and Measuring, p. 153				✓
	How Tall Would We Be?, p. 159			✓	
	Pass the Deck Operations, p. 166			✓	
	Pattern Chanting, p. 167			✓	
FRACTIONS	Sharing Milk, p. 168				✓
GEOMETRY	Fencing In an Area, p. 155				✓
	Pattern Chanting, p. 167			✓	
GRAPHS & DIAGRAMS	Bar Graphing Favorites, p. 147				✓
IDENTIFYING NUMBERS	Algebra Card Game, p. 143			✓	
IDENTIFYING SHAPES	Make a Polygon Animal, p. 161			✓	✓
	Spider Web, p. 170	✓		✓	
LINE SEGMENTS	Make a Line Segment Animal, p. 160			✓	✓
MATHEMATICAL DESCRIPTION	Newspaper Connections, p. 165		✓		✓
MEASUREMENT	Attribution Messages, p. 144				✓
	Estimating and Measuring, p. 153				✓
	Fencing In an Area, p. 155				✓
	How Tall Would We Be?, p. 159			✓	
	Make a Line Segment Animal, p. 160			✓	✓
	Spider Web, p. 170	✓		✓	
MENTAL MATH	Pass the Deck Operations, p. 166			✓	
	Pattern Chanting, p. 167			✓	

		GREETING	SHARING	GROUP ACTIVITY	MORNING MESSAGE
MONEY	Coin Combinations, p. 151				✓
	Making Change for a Dollar, p. 163				✓
MULTIPLICATION	Algebra Card Game, p. 143			✓	
	Battery Algebra, p. 149				✓
	How Many Ways, p. 158				✓
	Match Card Greeting, p. 164	✓			
	Pass the Deck Operations, p. 166			✓	
	Things in Groups #2, p. 173				✓
PART/WHOLE RELATIONSHIPS	Make a Polygon Animal, p. 161			✓	✓
PATTERNS	Pattern Chanting, p. 167			✓	
PLACE VALUE	Pattern Chanting, p. 167			✓	
PREDICTION	How Tall Would We Be?, p. 159			✓	
SORTING/ GROUPING	Attribution Messages, p. 144				✓
SUBTRACTION	Algebra Card Game, p. 143			✓	
	How Many Ways, p. 158				✓
	Match Card Greeting, p. 164	✓			
	Pass the Deck Operations, p. 166			✓	

Grade Level

5

	GREETING	SHARING	GROUP ACTIVITY	MORNING MESSAGE
ADDITION				
Continuous Sum Fractions, p. 179			✓	
Flip Card Game, p. 185			✓	
Group Memory, p. 187			✓	
Toss and Call with Numbers, p. 197			✓	
Toss and Call with Operations, p. 198			✓	
What's Our Sum Decimals, p. 202			✓	
What's Our Sum Fractions, p. 203			✓	
ATTRIBUTION				
Grab and Attribute, p. 186			✓	
AVERAGES				
Average Age, p. 175				✓
Batting Averages Message, p. 177				✓
COMPARISON				
Crane Problem, p. 180				✓
Matching and Drawing, p. 188			✓	
COUNTING				
Beach Raft Message, p. 178				✓
Mixed Number Making, p. 189			✓	
The Wall Message, p. 199				✓
DATA ANALYSIS				
Average Age, p. 175				✓
Beach Raft Message, p. 178				✓
Shooting Percentages, p. 195				✓
Snowman Message, p. 196				✓
The Wall Message, p. 199				✓
DECIMALS				
Matching and Drawing, p. 188			✓	
What's Our Sum Decimals, p. 202			✓	
DIVISION				
Flip Card Game, p. 185			✓	
Group Memory, p. 187			✓	
Toss and Call with Numbers, p. 197			✓	
Toss and Call with Operations, p. 198			✓	

Grade Level
5

	GREETING	SHARING	GROUP ACTIVITY	MORNING MESSAGE
ESTIMATION				
Crane Problem, p. 180				✓
Flip Card Game, p. 185			✓	
Group Memory, p. 187			✓	
Toss and Call with Numbers, p. 197			✓	
Toss and Call with Operations, p. 198			✓	
FRACTIONS				
Continuous Sum Fractions, p. 179			✓	
Matching and Drawing, p. 188			✓	
What's Our Sum Fractions, p. 203			✓	
GEOMETRY				
Finding Area and Perimeter, p. 183				✓
IDENTIFYING SHAPES				
Figure Making, p. 182				✓
Grab and Attribute, p. 186			✓	
MATHEMATICAL DESCRIPTION				
Describe the Item, p. 181			✓	
MEASUREMENT				
Beach Raft Message, p. 178				✓
Our Metric Heights, p. 192			✓	✓
Scaling Floor Layouts, p. 193		✓		
Snowman Message, p. 196				✓
The Wall Message, p. 199				✓
What Would Cover It?, p. 200			✓	
MENTAL MATH				
Toss and Call with Operations, p. 198			✓	
What's Our Sum Decimals, p. 202			✓	
What's Our Sum Fractions, p. 203			✓	

CONTINUED

		GREETING	SHARING	GROUP ACTIVITY	MORNING MESSAGE
MULTIPLICATION	Flip Card Game, p. 185			✓	
	Group Memory, p. 187			✓	
	Name Values Multiplication, p. 191				✓
	Toss and Call with Numbers, p. 197			✓	
	Toss and Call with Operations, p. 198			✓	
NUMBER RELATIONSHIPS	Flip Card Game, p. 185			✓	
	Toss and Call with Numbers, p. 197			✓	
	Which One Doesn't Belong?, p. 204				✓
PLACE VALUE	Mixed Number Making, p. 189			✓	
PREDICTION	Beach Raft Message, p. 178				✓
	Snowman Message, p. 196				✓
	The Wall Message, p. 199				✓
SUBTRACTION	Flip Card Game, p. 185			✓	
	Group Memory, p. 187			✓	
	Toss and Call with Numbers, p. 197			✓	
	Toss and Call with Operations, p. 198			✓	

Common Core Standards Correlation

Activity	Practices	Standards
All Grown Up, p. 13	2, 3, 4, 8	K.CC.1; K.CC.2; K.CC.3
Attribute Train, p. 14	5, 6, 7	K.MD.1; K.MD.2; K.G.2; K.G.4
Beats in a Name, p. 15 *Extension*	2, 4, 5, 6	K.CC.1; K.CC.4.a–c; K.OA.1 *K.OA.1; K.OA.2*
Collections Sharing, p. 16	2, 3, 6, 7	K.CC.1; K.CC.5; K.MD.1; K.MD.3
Dance with Me, p. 17	2, 4, 6	K.CC.1; K.CC.4a; K.G.1
Faster, Lower, Higher, p. 18	2, 4	K.MD.2
Fiddle Faddle, p. 19	1, 2, 4, 7	K.CC.2; K.CC.7
Growing Pattern Songs, p. 20 *Extension 2*	6, 7, 8	K.CC.1; K.CC.4a–c; K.OA.1 *K.OA.1*
I Spy a Shape, p. 22 *Extension 1*	2, 3, 4, 6, 7	K.MD.1; K.G.1; K.G.2 *K.MD.1; K.MD.3*
Lines, Lines Everywhere, p. 23 *Extension*	2, 3, 5, 6, 7	K.G.1; K.G.2 *K.G.5*
Number Lineup, p. 24	2, 4, 7	K.CC.1; K.CC.2; K.CC.4a–c; K.CC.5; K.CC.7
Number Line Walk, p. 25	2, 4, 5	K.CC.1; K.CC.2; K.CC.3; K.CC.4a–c; K.CC.5; K.OA.1; K.OA.2
Numbers in My House, p. 26 *Extension*	4, 7	K.MD.3 *K.CC.3*
Odd or Even, p. 27 *Extension*	1, 2, 4, 5, 7	K.OA.1; K.OA.2 *K.CC.1; K.CC.3; K.CC.4a; K.OA.1; K.OA.5*
Patterns Around the Circle, p. 28	2, 4, 5, 6	K.CC.4b; K.OA.1

Activity	Practices	Standards
Plus/Minus, p. 29 *Variation* *Extension*	1, 2, 4, 5, 6	K.CC.1; K.CC.4a–c; K.CC.5; K.CC.6; K.OA.1; K.OA.5 *K.MD.2; K.G.5* *K.CC.3*
Shoe Graph, p. 30	2, 6, 7	K.CC.1; K.CC.5; K.CC.6; K.MD.3
Shorter/Longer, p. 31	2, 4, 5, 7	K.CC.4a–c; K.CC.6; K.MD.1; K.MD.2; K.MD.3
Skip Greeting, p. 32	1, 2, 6, 7, 8	K.CC.4a–c; K.OA.1
So Does Mine, p. 33	3, 6, 7	K.CC.3; K.CC.6; K.MD.1; K.MD.3
String Shapes, p. 35	1, 5, 7	K.MD.2; K.G.2; K.G.4; K.G.5
Time to . . . , p. 37	2, 3, 4, 6, 7	K.CC.3
Under the Cup, p. 38	1, 2, 6	K.CC.3; K.CC.7
Yes/No Questions, p. 39	1, 2, 3, 5, 6	K.CC.4.a–c; K.CC.5; K.CC.6; K.OA.1
Zero Sharing, p. 41	2, 3	K.CC.3

Practice	Activities
1 Make sense of problems and persevere in solving them.	Fiddle Faddle, p. 19; Odd or Even, p. 27; Plus/Minus, p. 29; Skip Greeting, p. 32; String Shapes, p. 35; Under the Cup, p. 38; Yes/No Questions, p. 39
2 Reason abstractly and quantitatively.	All Grown Up, p. 13; Beats in a Name, p. 15; Collections Sharing, p. 16; Dance with Me, p. 17; Faster, Lower, Higher, p. 18; Fiddle Faddle, p. 19; I Spy a Shape, p. 22; Lines, Lines Everywhere, p. 23; Number Lineup, p. 24; Number Line Walk, p. 25; Odd or Even, p. 27; Patterns Around the Circle, p. 28; Plus/Minus, p. 29; Shoe Graph, p. 30; Shorter/Longer, p. 31; Skip Greeting, p. 32; Time to . . . , p. 37; Under the Cup, p. 38; Yes/No Questions, p. 39; Zero Sharing, p. 41
3 Construct viable arguments and critique the reasoning of others.	All Grown Up, p. 13; Collections Sharing, p. 16; I Spy a Shape, p. 22; Lines, Lines Everywhere, p. 23; So Does Mine, p. 33; Time to . . . , p. 37; Yes/No Questions, p. 39; Zero Sharing, p. 41
4 Model with mathematics.	All Grown Up, p. 13; Beats in a Name, p. 15; Dance with Me, p. 17; Faster, Lower, Higher, p. 18; Fiddle Faddle, p. 19; I Spy a Shape, p. 22; Number Lineup, p. 24; Number Line Walk, p. 25; Numbers in My House, p. 26; Odd or Even, p. 27; Patterns Around the Circle, p. 28; Plus/Minus, p. 29; Shorter/Longer, p. 31; Time to . . . , p. 37
5 Use appropriate tools strategically.	Attribute Train, p. 14; Beats in a Name, p. 15; Lines, Lines Everywhere, p. 23; Number Line Walk, p. 25; Odd or Even, p. 27; Patterns Around the Circle, p. 28; Plus/Minus, p. 29; Shorter/Longer, p. 31; String Shapes, p. 35; Yes/No Questions, p. 39
6 Attend to precision.	Attribute Train, p. 14; Beats in a Name, p. 15; Collections Sharing, p. 16; Dance with Me, p. 17; Growing Pattern Songs, p. 20; I Spy a Shape, p. 22; Lines, Lines Everywhere, p. 23; Patterns Around the Circle, p. 28; Plus/Minus, p. 29; Shoe Graph, p. 30; Skip Greeting, p. 32; So Does Mine, p. 33; Time to . . . , p. 37; Under the Cup, p. 38; Yes/No Questions, p. 39
7 Look for and make use of structure.	Attribute Train, p. 14; Collections Sharing, p. 16; Fiddle Faddle, p. 19; Growing Pattern Songs, p. 20; I Spy a Shape, p. 22; Lines, Lines Everywhere, p. 23; Number Lineup, p. 24; Numbers in My House, p. 26; Odd or Even, p. 27; Shoe Graph, p. 30; Shorter/Longer, p. 31; Skip Greeting, p. 32; So Does Mine, p. 33; Time to . . . , p. 37; String Shapes, p. 35
8 Look for and express regularity in repeated reasoning.	All Grown Up, p. 13; Growing Pattern Songs, p. 20; Skip Greeting, p. 32

Standards	Activities
K.CC.1 • Count to 100 by ones and by tens	All Grown Up, p. 13; Beats in a Name, p. 15; Collections Sharing, p. 16; Dance with Me, p. 17; Growing Pattern Songs, p. 20; Number Lineup, p. 24; Number Line Walk, p. 25; Odd or Even (extension), p. 27; Plus/Minus, p. 29; Shoe Graph, p. 30
K.CC.2 • Count forward beginning from a given number within the known sequence	All Grown Up, p. 13; Fiddle Faddle, p. 19; Number Lineup, p. 24; Number Line Walk, p. 25
K.CC.3 • Write numbers from 0 to 20; represent a number of objects with a written numeral 0–20	All Grown Up, p. 13; Number Line Walk, p. 25; Numbers in My House (extension), p. 26; Plus/Minus (extension), p. 29; So Does Mine, p. 33; Time to . . . , p. 37; Under the Cup, p. 38; Zero Sharing, p. 41
K.CC.4a–c • Understand the relationship between numbers and quantities; when counting objects, say number names in standard order; understand the last number name; understand each successive number name	Beats in a Name, p. 15; Dance with Me, p. 17 (a only); Growing Pattern Songs, p. 20; Number Lineup, p. 24; Number Line Walk, p. 25; Odd or Even (extension), p. 27 (a only); Patterns Around the Circle, p. 28 (b only); Plus/Minus, p. 29; Shorter/Longer, p. 31; Skip Greeting, p. 32; Yes/No Questions, p. 39
K.CC.5 • Count to answer "how many?" questions	Collections Sharing, p. 16; Number Lineup, p. 24; Number Line Walk, p. 25; Plus/Minus, p. 29; Shoe Graph, p. 30, Yes/No Questions, p. 39
K.CC.6 • Identify whether the number of objects in one group is greater than, less than, or equal to the number of objects in another group	Plus/Minus, p. 29; Shoe Graph, p. 30; Shorter/Longer, p. 31; So Does Mine, p. 33; Yes/No Questions, p. 39
K.CC.7 • Compare two numbers between 1 and 10	Fiddle Faddle, p. 19; Number Lineup, p. 24; Under the Cup, p. 38
K.OA.1 • Represent addition and subtraction with objects, fingers, mental images, drawings, sounds	Beats in a Name, p. 15; Growing Pattern Songs, p. 20; Number Line Walk, p. 25; Odd or Even, p. 27; Patterns Around the Circle, p. 28; Plus/Minus, p. 29; Skip Greeting, p. 32; Yes/No Questions, p. 39
K.OA.2 • Solve addition and subtraction word problems	Beats in a Name (extension), p. 15; Number Line Walk, p. 25; Odd or Even, p. 27
K.OA.3	None
K.OA.4	None
K.OA.5 • Fluently add and subtract within 5	Odd or Even (extension), p. 27; Plus/Minus, p. 29
K.NBT.1	None

225

Standards	Activities
K.MD.1 • Describe measurable attributes of objects, such as length or weight	Attribute Train, p. 14; Collections Sharing, p. 16; I Spy a Shape, p. 22; Shorter/Longer, p. 31; So Does Mine, p. 33
K.MD.2 • Directly compare two objects with a measurable attribute in common	Attribute Train, p. 14; Faster, Lower, Higher, p. 18; Plus/Minus (variation), p. 29; Shorter/Longer, p. 31; String Shapes, p. 35
K.MD.3 • Classify objects into given categories; count the numbers of objects in each category	Collections Sharing, p. 16; I Spy a Shape (extension 1), p. 22; Numbers in My House, p. 26; Shoe Graph, p. 30; Shorter/Longer, p. 31; So Does Mine, p. 33
K.G.1 • Describe objects in the environment using names of shapes	Dance with Me, p. 17; I Spy a Shape, p. 22; Lines, Lines Everywhere, p. 23
K.G.2 • Correctly name shapes regardless of their orientation or overall size	Attribute Train, p. 14; I Spy a Shape, p. 22; Lines, Lines Everywhere, p. 23; String Shapes, p. 35
K.G.3	None
K.G.4 • Analyze and compare two- and three-dimensional shapes	Attribute Train, p. 14; String Shapes, p. 35
K.G.5 • Model shapes in the world by building shapes from components . . . and drawing shapes	Lines, Lines Everywhere (extension), p. 23; Plus/Minus (variation), p. 29; String Shapes, p. 35
K.G.6	None

Activity	Practices	Standards
Adding Our Way to 100, p. 43 *Variation/Extension*	1, 2, 3, 5, 6 *4, 7, 8*	K1.OA.1; 1.OA.5; 1.OA.6; 1.NBT.1; 1.NBT.2a–c; 1.NBT.4; 1.NBT.5
Beanbag Toss, p. 45 *Variation*	1, 3, 4, 5, 7	1.OA.1; 1.OA.3; 1.OA.6 *1.OA.7*
Card Greeting, p. 46	2, 3, 8	1.OA.1; 1.OA.5; 1.NBT.2a
Class Detectives, p. 47 *Extensions*	1, 2, 4, 5, 6	1.OA.5; 1.NBT.3; 1.MD.4 *1.MD.2*
A Clip and Save Meeting, p. 48	1, 2, 3, 4, 6	1.OA.1; 1.OA.2; 1.OA.5; 1.NBT.1; 1.NBT.2a,c; 1.NBT.3; 1.NBT.4; 1.MD.4
Dice Greeting, p. 50	2, 3, 7, 8	1.OA.1; 1.OA.5
Favorites Graph, p. 51	2, 4, 5, 6, 7	1.NBT.3; 1.MD.4
How Many to Ten?, p. 52	1, 2, 4, 6, 8	1.OA.1; 1.OA.2; 1.OA.3; 1.OA.4; 1.OA.5; 1.OA.6; 1.OA.7; 1.OA.8
How Much Space?, p. 53 *Variations* *Extensions*	1, 3, 4, 5, 7	1.OA.1; 1.OA.5; 1.MD.4 *1.MD.2; 1.G.2* *1.G.2*
Hundreds Chart Paths, p. 54	1, 2, 4, 5, 8	1.NBT.2a–c; 1.NBT.3; 1.NBT.5; 1.NBT.6
If I Were One Inch Tall, p. 55	3, 4, 5, 6, 7	1.MD.1; 1.MD.2; 1.MD.4
Magic Doubles, p. 56	2, 3, 4, 6, 7	1.OA.1; 1.OA.3; 1.OA.6; 1.OA.7; 1.OA.8; 1.MD.4
Make a Shape, p. 58 *Variation*	1, 6, 7	1.G.1; 1.G.2 *1.G.3*
Measuring in Tens and Ones, p. 60	1, 4, 5, 7, 8	1.OA.5; 1.NBT.2a–c; 1.MD.2; 1.MD.4
Number Grid Puzzle, p. 61	3, 4, 6, 7, 8	1.NBT.1; 1.NBT.2; 1.NBT.3; 1.NBT.5; 1.NBT.6
Pattern of the Day, p. 62	2, 6, 7, 8	1.OA.5
Quarters, p. 63	1, 2, 3, 4, 8	1.OA.1; 1.OA.2; 1.OA.3; 1.OA.5; 1.OA.6; 1.NBT.2a–c; 1.NBT.3

Activity	Practices	Standards
Scoop 'Em Up, p. 64	1, 3, 4, 6, 8	1.OA.3; 1.OA.5; 1.NBT.1; 1.NBT.2a–c; 1.NBT.4; 1.MD.4
Seconds, Minutes, Hours, p. 66	2, 3, 4, 5, 6	1.OA.5; 1.NBT.2c; 1.NBT.4
Shape Hunt, p. 68	3, 6, 7	1.MD.4; 1.G.1
Start with Ten, p. 69	2, 5, 6, 8	1.OA.1; 1.OA.3; 1.OA.5; 1.OA.6; 1.NBT.2a, b; 1.NBT.4
This Group, That Group, p. 70 *Variations/Extension*	3, 7	1.MD.4 *1.G.1*
Tiles in a Bag, p. 71	1, 2, 3, 6, 8	1.OA.1; 1.OA.2; 1.OA.3; 1.OA.4; 1.OA.5; 1.OA.6; 1.OA.8; 1.MD.4
A Trail Mix Recipe, p. 72	2, 3, 4, 5, 6	I.OA.1; 1.OA.2; 1.OA.3; 1.OA.4; 1.OA.5; 1.OA.6; 1.MD.4
Two Is King, p. 73	2, 3, 6, 7	1.OA.1; 1.OA.3; 1.OA.4; 1.OA.5; 1.OA.6; 1.OA.8; 1.NBT.2b; 1.NBT.4

Practice	Activities
1 Make sense of problems and persevere in solving them.	Adding Our Way to 100, p. 43; Beanbag Toss, p. 45; Class Detectives, p. 47; A Clip and Save Meeting, p. 48; How Many to Ten?, p. 52; How Much Space?, p. 53; Hundreds Chart Paths, p. 54; Make a Shape, p. 58; Measuring in Tens and Ones, p. 60; Quarters, p. 63; Scoop 'Em Up, p. 64; Tiles in a Bag, p. 71
2 Reason abstractly and quantitatively.	Adding Our Way to 100, p. 43; Card Greeting, p. 46; Class Detectives, p. 47; A Clip and Save Meeting, p. 48; Dice Greeting, p. 50; Favorites Graph, p. 51; How Many to Ten?, p. 52; Hundreds Chart Paths, p. 54; Magic Doubles, p. 56; Pattern of the Day, p. 62; Quarters, p. 63; Seconds, Minutes, Hours, p. 66; Start with Ten, p 69; Tiles in a Bag, p. 71; A Trail Mix Recipe, p. 72; Two Is King, p. 73
3 Construct viable arguments and critique the reasoning of others.	Adding Our Way to 100, p. 43; Beanbag Toss, p. 45; Card Greeting, p. 46; A Clip and Save Meeting, p. 48; Dice Greeting, p. 50; How Much Space?, p. 53; If I Were One Inch Tall, p. 55; Magic Doubles, p. 56; Number Grid Puzzle, p. 61; Quarters, p. 63; Scoop 'Em Up, p. 64; Seconds, Minutes, Hours, p. 66; Shape Hunt, p. 68; This Group, That Group, p. 70; Tiles in a Bag, p. 71; A Trail Mix Recipe, p. 72; Two Is King, p. 73
4 Model with mathematics.	Adding Our Way to 100 (variation/extension), p. 43; Beanbag Toss, p. 45; Class Detectives, p. 47; A Clip and Save Meeting, p. 48; Favorites Graph, p. 51; How Many to Ten?, p. 52; How Much Space?, p. 53; Hundreds Chart Paths, p. 54; If I Were One Inch Tall, p. 55; Magic Doubles, p. 56; Measuring in Tens and Ones, p. 60; Number Grid Puzzle, p. 61; Quarters, p. 63; Scoop 'Em Up, p. 64; Seconds, Minutes, Hours, p. 66; A Trail Mix Recipe, p. 72
5 Use appropriate tools strategically.	Adding Our Way to 100, p. 43; Beanbag Toss, p. 45; Class Detectives, p. 47; Favorites Graph, p. 51; How Much Space?, p. 53; Hundreds Chart Paths, p. 54; If I Were One Inch Tall, p. 55; Measuring in Tens and Ones, p. 60; Seconds, Minutes, Hours, p. 66; Start with Ten, p. 69; A Trail Mix Recipe, p. 72
6 Attend to precision.	Adding Our Way to 100, p. 43; Class Detectives, p. 47; A Clip and Save Meeting, p. 48; Favorites Graph, p. 51; How Many to Ten?, p. 52; If I Were One Inch Tall, p. 55; Magic Doubles, p. 56; Make a Shape, p. 58; Number Grid Puzzle, p. 61; Pattern of the Day, p. 62; Scoop 'Em Up, p. 64; Seconds, Minutes, Hours, p. 66; Shape Hunt, p. 68; Start with Ten, p. 69; Tiles in a Bag, p. 71; A Trail Mix Recipe, p. 72; Two Is King, p. 73
7 Look for and make use of structure.	Adding Our Way to 100 (variation/extension), p. 43; Beanbag Toss, p. 45; Dice Greeting, p. 50; Favorites Graph, p. 51; How Much Space?, p. 53; If I Were One Inch Tall, p. 55; Magic Doubles, p. 56; Make a Shape, p. 58; Measuring in Tens and Ones, p. 60; Number Grid Puzzle, p. 61; Pattern of the Day, p. 62; Shape Hunt, p. 68; This Group, That Group, p. 70; Two Is King, p. 73
8 Look for and express regularity in repeated reasoning.	Adding Our Way to 100 (variation/extension), p. 43; Card Greeting, p. 46; Dice Greeting, p. 50; How Many to Ten?, p. 52; Hundreds Chart Paths, p. 54; Measuring in Tens and Ones, p. 60; Number Grid Puzzle, p. 61; Pattern of the Day, p. 62; Quarters, p. 63; Scoop 'Em Up, p. 64; Start with Ten, p. 69; Tiles in a Bag, p. 71

Common Core Correlation by Mathematical **Standards**

Standards	Activities
1.OA.1 Use addition and subtraction within 20 to solve word problems	Adding Our Way to 100, p. 43; Beanbag Toss, p. 45; Card Greeting, p. 46; A Clip and Save Meeting, p. 48; Dice Greeting, p. 50; How Many to Ten?, p. 52; How Much Space?, p. 53; Magic Doubles, p. 56; Quarters, p. 63; Start with Ten, p. 69; Tiles in a Bag, p. 71; A Trail Mix Recipe, p. 72; Two Is King, p. 73
1.OA.2 Solve word problems that call for addition of three whole numbers	A Clip and Save Meeting, p. 48; How Many to Ten?, p. 52; Quarters, p. 63; Tiles in a Bag, p. 71; A Trail Mix Recipe, p. 72
1.OA.3 Apply properties of operations as strategies to add and subtract	Beanbag Toss, p. 45; How Many to Ten?, p. 52; Magic Doubles, p. 56; Quarters, p. 63; Scoop 'Em Up, p. 64; Start with Ten, p. 69; Tiles in a Bag, p. 71; A Trail Mix Recipe, p. 72; Two Is King, p. 73
1.OA.4 Understand subtraction as an unknown-addend problem	How Many to Ten?, p. 52; Tiles in a Bag, p. 71; A Trail Mix Recipe, p. 72; Two Is King, p. 73
1.OA.5 Relate counting to addition and subtraction	Adding Our Way to 100, p. 43; Card Greeting, p. 46; Class Detectives, p. 47; A Clip and Save Meeting, p. 48; Dice Greeting, p. 50; How Many to Ten?, p. 52; How Much Space?, p. 53; Measuring in Tens and Ones, p. 60; Pattern of the Day, p. 62; Quarters, p. 63; Scoop 'Em Up, p. 64; Seconds, Minutes, Hours, p. 66; Start with Ten, p. 69; Tiles in a Bag, p. 71; A Trail Mix Recipe, p. 72; Two Is King, p. 73
1.OA.6 Add and subtract within 20	Adding Our Way to 100, p. 43; Beanbag Toss, p. 45; How Many to Ten?, p. 52; Magic Doubles, p. 56; Quarters, p. 63; Start with Ten, p. 69; Tiles in a Bag, p. 71; A Trail Mix Recipe, p. 72; Two Is King, p. 73
1.OA.7 Understand the meaning of the equal sign	Beanbag Toss (variation), p. 45; How Many to Ten?, p. 52; Magic Doubles, p. 56
1.OA.8 Determine the unknown . . . in an addition or subtraction equation	How Many to Ten?, p. 52; Magic Doubles, p. 56; Tiles in a Bag, p. 71; Two Is King, p. 73
1.NBT.1 Count to 120, starting at any number less than 120	Adding Our Way to 100, p. 43; A Clip and Save Meeting, p. 48; Number Grid Puzzle, p. 61; Scoop 'Em Up, p. 64
1.NBT.2 Understand that the two digits of a two-digit number represent amounts of tens and ones	Number Grid Puzzle, p. 61
1.NBT.2a–c Understand 10; the numbers from 11 to 19; the numbers 10, 20, 30, 40, 50, 60, 70, 80, 90	Adding Our Way to 100, p. 43; Card Greeting, p. 46 (a only); A Clip and Save Meeting, p. 48 (a, c only); Hundreds Chart Paths, p. 54; Measuring in Tens and Ones, p. 60; Quarters, p. 63; Scoop 'Em Up, p. 64; Seconds, Minutes, Hours, p. 66 (c only); Start with Ten, p. 69 (a, b only); Two Is King, p. 73 (b only)

Common Core Correlation by Mathematical **Standards**, cont.

Standards	Activities
1.NBT.3 Compare two two-digit numbers	Class Detectives, p. 47; A Clip and Save Meeting, p. 48; Favorites Graph, p. 51; Hundreds Chart Paths, p. 54; Number Grid Puzzle, p. 61; Quarters, p. 63
1.NBT.4 Add within 100	Adding Our Way to 100, p. 43; A Clip and Save Meeting, p. 48; Scoop 'Em Up, p. 64; Seconds, Minutes, Hours, p. 66; Start with Ten, p. 69; Two Is King, p. 73
1.NBT.5 Mentally find 10 more or 10 less than a two-digit number	Adding Our Way to 100, p. 43; Hundreds Chart Paths, p. 54; Number Grid Puzzle, p. 61
1.NBT.6 Subtract multiples of 10	Hundreds Chart Paths, p. 54; Number Grid Puzzle, p. 61
1.MD.1 Order three objects by length	If I Were One Inch Tall, p. 55
1.MD.2 Express the length of an object as a whole number of length units	How Much Space? (variations), p. 53; If I Were One Inch Tall, p. 55; Measuring in Tens and Ones, p. 60
1.MD.3	None
1.MD.4 Organize, represent, and interpret data with up to three categories	Class Detectives, p. 47; A Clip and Save Meeting, p. 48; Favorites Graph, p. 51; How Much Space?, p. 53; If I Were One Inch Tall, p. 55; Magic Doubles, p. 56; Measuring in Tens and Ones, p. 60; Scoop 'Em Up, p. 64; Shape Hunt, p. 68; This Group, That Group, p. 70; Tiles in a Bag, p. 71; A Trail Mix Recipe, p. 72
1.G.1 Distinguish between defining attributes . . . versus non-defining attributes	Make a Shape, p. 58; Shape Hunt, p. 68; This Group, That Group (variations, extension), p. 70
1.G.2 Compose two-dimensional . . . or three-dimensional shapes	How Much Space? (variations, extensions), p. 53; Make a Shape, p. 58
1.G.3 Partition circles and rectangles into two and four equal shares	Make a Shape (variation), p. 58

Activity	Practice	Standards
Are You a Rectangle?, p. 75 *Extension 1*	2, 4, 5, 7	2.G.1 *2.MD.1; 2.MD.4; 2.MD.9*
Bouncing Balls, p. 76	2, 3, 4, 5	2.OA.2; 2.MD.10
Broken Calculator, p. 78	1, 2, 3, 5, 8	2.OA.1; 2.OA.2; 2.NBT.5; 2.NBT.9
Card Combination Game, p. 79	2, 6, 7	2.OA.2; 2.NBT.5
Catch the Bug, p. 80	1, 2, 6	2.OA.1; 2.OA.2; 2.NBT.5
Give It Time, p. 81	3, 4	2.MD.10
Graphing Pockets, p. 82 *Extension 1*	1, 2, 3, 4, 5 6	2.OA.1; 2.OA.2; 2.MD.10 *2.NBT.1; 2.NBT.5*
Guess My Number, p. 84	2, 3, 6, 8	2.OA.1; 2.NBT.1a; 2.NBT.2; 2.NBT.5
Guess *Your* Number, p. 85	2, 3, 6, 8	2.OA.1; 2.OA.2; 2.NBT.1; 2.NBT.4
Guess *Your* Shape, p. 86 *Variation 2*	1, 2, 3, 7	2.G.1 *2.G.3*
Human Polygons, p. 87	1, 2, 3, 6, 7	2.G.1
It Could Be a . . . , p. 89	2, 3, 5, 6, 7	2.G.1
Magic 20, p. 90	1, 2, 3, 6	2.OA.1; 2.OA.2
Make the Number, p. 91 *Variations/Extensions*	1, 2, 6	2.NBT.3 *2.NBT.1a, b; 2.NBT.4*
Math Book Sharing, p. 92	3, 4, 7 (others, depending upon book chosen)	Varies depending upon book chosen
Measure Yourself, p. 94	2, 3, 4, 5, 6	2.MD.1; 2.MD.2; 2.MD.3; 2.MD.4
Money for Nothin', p. 95	1, 2, 3, 4, 8	2.OA.1; 2.OA.2; 2.NBT.1a, b; 2.NBT.4; 2.NBT.5; 2.NBT.6; 2.NBT.8; 2.NBT.9; 2.MD.8

Activity	Practice	Standards
Name Patterns, p. 96	1, 2, 3, 4, 5	2.OA.1; 2.OA.4
Name Values, p. 97 *Variation 3* *Extension 3*	1, 2, 3, 4, 6	2.OA.1; 2.OA.2; 2.NBT.1a, b; 2.NBT.3; 2.NBT.5; 2.NBT.6; 2.NBT.7; 2.NBT.9 *2.MD.8* *2.MD.10*
Roll a Big One, p. 98 *Variation*	1, 2, 3, 4, 6	2.OA.1; 2.NBT.3 *2.NBT.1a, b; 2.NBT.3; 2.NBT.4*
Six Rolls to 100, p. 100	1, 2, 3, 4, 5	2.OA.1; 2.OA.2; 2.NBT.1, 1a; 2.NBT.5; 2.NBT.9
Skip Greeting with Cards, p. 102	2, 6, 8	2.OA.1; 2.OA.2; 2.NBT.2
Spinners, p. 103	2, 3, 4, 6	2.OA.1; 2.OA.2; 2.OA.4; 2.MD.10
Venn Diagrams, p. 104 *Extension 1* *Extension 3*	2, 3, 4, 6, 7	2.OA.1; 2.OA.2; 2.MD.10 *2.G.1* *2.MD.1; 2.MD.2; 2.MD.4*
What Number Am I?, p. 107	1, 2, 4, 6, 8	2.OA.1; 2.OA.2; 2.NBT.5; 2.NBT.9

Practice	Activities
1 Make sense of problems and persevere in solving them.	Broken Calculator, p. 78; Catch the Bug, p. 80; Graphing Pockets, p. 82; Guess Your Shape, p. 86; Human Polygons, p. 87; Magic 20, p. 90; Make the Number, p. 91; Money for Nothin', p. 95; Name Patterns, p. 96; Name Values, p. 97; Roll a Big One, p. 98; Six Rolls to 100, p. 100; What Number Am I?, p. 107
2 Reason abstractly and quantitatively.	Are You a Rectangle?, p. 75; Bouncing Balls, p. 76; Broken Calculator, p. 78; Card Combination Game, p. 79; Catch the Bug, p. 80; Graphing Pockets, p. 82; Guess My Number, p. 84; Guess Your Number, p. 85; Guess Your Shape, p. 86; Human Polygons, p. 87; It Could Be a . . . , p. 89; Magic 20, p. 90; Make the Number, p. 91; Measure Yourself, p. 94; Money for Nothin', p. 95; Name Patterns, p. 96; Name Values, p. 97; Roll a Big One, p. 98; Six Rolls to 100, p. 100; Skip Greeting with Cards, p. 102; Spinners, p. 103; Venn Diagrams, p. 104; What Number Am I?, p. 107
3 Construct viable arguments and critique the reasoning of others.	Bouncing Balls, p. 76; Broken Calculator, p. 78; Give It Time, p. 81; Graphing Pockets, p. 82; Guess My Number, p. 84; Guess Your Number, p. 85; Guess Your Shape, p. 86; Human Polygons, p. 87; It Could Be a . . . , p. 89; Magic 20, p. 90; Math Book Sharing, p. 92; Measure Yourself, p. 94; Money for Nothin', p. 95; Name Patterns, p. 96; Name Values, p. 97; Roll a Big One, p. 98; Six Rolls to 100, p. 100; Spinners, p. 103; Venn Diagrams, p. 104
4 Model with mathematics.	Are You a Rectangle?, p. 75; Bouncing Balls, p. 76; Give It Time, p. 81; Graphing Pockets, p. 82; Math Book Sharing, p. 92; Measure Yourself, p. 94; Money for Nothin', p. 95; Name Patterns, p. 96; Name Values, p. 97; Roll a Big One, p. 98; Six Rolls to 100, p. 100; Spinners, p. 103; Venn Diagrams, p. 104; What Number Am I?, p. 107
5 Use appropriate tools strategically.	Are You a Rectangle?, p. 75; Bouncing Balls, p. 76; Broken Calculator, p. 78; Graphing Pockets, p. 82; It Could Be a . . . , p. 89; Measure Yourself, p. 94; Name Patterns, p. 96; Six Rolls to 100, p. 100
6 Attend to precision.	Card Combination Game, p. 79; Catch the Bug, p. 80; Graphing Pockets (extension 1), p. 82; Guess My Number, p. 84; Guess Your Number, p. 85; Human Polygons, p. 87; It Could Be a . . . , p. 89; Magic 20, p. 90; Make the Number, p. 91; Measure Yourself, p. 94; Name Values, p. 97; Roll a Big One, p. 98; Skip Greeting with Cards, p. 102; Spinners, p. 103; Venn Diagrams, p. 104; What Number Am I?, p. 107
7 Look for and make use of structure.	Are You a Rectangle?, p. 75; Card Combination Game, p. 79; Guess Your Shape, p. 86; Human Polygons, p. 87; It Could Be a . . . , p. 89; Math Book Sharing, p. 92; Venn Diagrams, p. 104
8 Look for and express regularity in repeated reasoning.	Broken Calculator, p. 78; Guess My Number, p. 84; Guess *Your* Number, p. 85; Money for Nothin', p. 95; Skip Greeting with Cards, p. 102; What Number Am I?, p. 107

Standards	Activities
2.OA.1 • Use addition and subtraction within 100 to solve one- and two-step word problems	Broken Calculator, p. 78; Catch the Bug, p. 80; Graphing Pockets, p. 82; Guess My Number, p. 84; Guess *Your* Number, p. 85; Magic 20, p. 90; Money for Nothin', p. 95; Name Patterns, p. 96; Name Values, p. 97; Roll a Big One, p. 98; Six Rolls to 100, p. 100; Skip Greeting with Cards, p. 102; Spinners, p. 103; Venn Diagrams, p. 104; What Number Am I?, p. 107
2.OA.2 • Fluently add and subtract within 20 using mental strategies	Bouncing Balls, p. 76; Broken Calculator, p. 78; Card Combination Game, p. 79; Catch the Bug, p. 80; Graphing Pockets, p. 82; Guess *Your* Number, p. 85; Magic 20, p. 90; Money for Nothin', p. 95; Name Values, p. 97; Six Rolls to 100, p. 100; Skip Greeting with Cards, p. 102; Spinners, p. 103; Venn Diagrams, p. 104; What Number Am I?, p. 107
2.OA.3	None
2.OA.4 Use addition to find the total number of objects arranged in rectangular arrays	Name Patterns, p. 96; Spinners, p. 103
2.NBT.1 Understand . . . hundreds, tens, and ones	Graphing Pockets (extension 1), p. 82; Guess Your Number, p. 85; Six Rolls to 100, p. 100
2.NBT.1a–b Understand 100; the numbers 100, 200, 300, 400, 500, 600, 700, 800, 900	Guess My Number, p. 84 (a only); Make the Number (variations/extensions), p. 91; Money for Nothin', p. 95; Name Values, p. 97; Roll a Big One (variation), p. 98; Six Rolls to 100, p. 100 (a only)
2.NBT.2 Count within 1000	Guess My Number, p. 84; Skip Greeting with Cards, p. 102
2.NBT.3 Read and write numbers to 1000	Make the Number, p. 91; Name Values, p. 97; Roll a Big One, p. 98
2.NBT.4 Compare two three-digit numbers	Guess *Your* Number, p. 85; Make the Number (variations/extensions), p. 91; Money for Nothin', p. 95; Roll a Big One (variation), p. 98
2.NBT.5 Fluently add and subtract within 100	Broken Calculator, p. 78; Card Combination Game, p. 79; Catch the Bug, p. 80; Graphing Pockets (extension 1), p. 82; Guess My Number, p. 84; Money for Nothin', p. 95; Name Values, p. 97; Six Rolls to 100, p. 100; What Number Am I?, p. 107
2.NBT.6 Add up to four two-digit numbers	Money for Nothin', p. 95; Name Values, p. 97
2.NBT.7 Add and subtract within 1000	Name Values, p. 97

Standards	Activities
2.NBT.8 Mentally add . . . and mentally subtract 10 or 100 from a given number 100–900	Money for Nothin', p. 95
2.NBT.9 Explain why addition and subtraction strategies work	Broken Calculator, p. 78; Money for Nothin', p. 95; Name Values, p. 97; Six Rolls to 100, p. 100; What Number Am I?, p. 107
2.MD.1 Measure the length of an object	Are You a Rectangle? (extension 1), p. 75; Measure Yourself, p. 94; Venn Diagrams (extension 3), p. 104
2.MD.2 Measure the length of an object twice	Measure Yourself, p. 94; Venn Diagrams (extension 3), p. 104
2.MD.3 Estimate lengths	Measure Yourself, p. 94
2.MD.4 Measure to determine how much longer one object is than another	Are You a Rectangle? (extension 1), p. 75; Measure Yourself, p. 94; Venn Diagrams (extension 3), p. 104
2.MD.5	None
2.MD.6	None
2.MD.7	None
2.MD.8 Solve word problems involving dollar bills, quarters, dimes, nickels, and pennies	Money for Nothin', p. 95; Name Values (variation 3), p. 97
2.MD.9 Generate measurement data	Are You a Rectangle? (extension 1), p. 75
2.MD.10 Draw a picture graph and a bar graph . . . to represent a data set	Bouncing Balls, p. 76; Give It Time, p. 81; Graphing Pockets, p. 82; Name Values (extension 3), p. 97; Spinners, p. 103; Venn Diagrams, p. 104
2.G.1 Recognize and draw shapes having specified attributes	Are You a Rectangle?, p. 75; Guess Your Shape, p. 86; Human Polygons, p. 87; It Could Be a . . . , p. 89; Venn Diagrams (extension 1), p. 104
2.G.2	None
2.G.3 Partition circles and rectangles into two, three, or four equal shares	Guess *Your* Shape (variation 2), p. 86

3 Common Core Math Correlation by **Activities**

Activity	Practices	Standards
Base Ten Block Building, p. 109 *Variation 2*	1, 2, 4, 5, 7	3.NBT.1; 3.NBT.2 *3.OA.1; 3.OA.3; 3.OA.4; 3.OA.5; 3.OA.7; 3.NBT.3*
Beach Ball Tossing, p. 110 *Variations*	2, 4, 6	3.OA.1; 3.OA.4; 3.OA.5; 3.OA.7; 3.NBT.2; 3.NBT.3 *3.NF.1; 3.NF.3a–d*
Body Math, p. 111	1, 2, 6, 7	3.OA.3; 3.OA.6; 3.NF.1; 3.NF.3a–d
Clock Check-In, p. 112 *Extension*	2, 3, 6 *4*	3.MD.1 *3.MD.3*
Coin Flip Probability, p. 114	2, 3, 4, 6, 7	3.OA.9; 3.NBT.2; 3.MD.3
Digit Pop, p. 115	2, 3, 6, 7	3.OA.9; 3.NBT.2
Dimensions in the Bubble, p. 116	1, 2, 3, 5, 6	3.OA.3; 3.OA.4; 3.OA.7; 3.NF.1; 3.MD.4; 3.MD.5a–b; 3.MD.6; 3.MD.7a–d; 3.MD.8
Double This, p. 118	1, 2, 6, 8	3.OA.1; 3.OA.3; 3.OA.4; 3.OA.7; 3.OA.9
Equations and Pictures, p. 119 *Variation*	1, 2, 3, 4, 6	3.OA.1; 3.OA.3; 3.OA.4; 3.OA.5; 3.OA.7; 3.OA.9 *3.NF.1; 3.NF.3a–d*
Examining Temperatures, p. 120	2, 3, 4, 7	3.OA.9; 3.NBT.2; 3.MD.3
How Long Will It Bounce?, p. 122 *Extension*	2, 3, 5 *4*	3.OA.8; 3.NBT.2; 3.MD.1 *3.MD.3*
How Much Money?, p. 123	2, 3, 4, 5, 6	3.OA.1; 3.OA.3; 3.OA.4; 3.OA.5; 3.OA.7; 3.OA.8; 3.OA.9; 3.NBT.2; 3.NBT.3; 3.NF.1
Isosceles Triangle Message, p. 124	1, 2, 5, 6, 7	3.G.1; 3.G.2
Magical Mystery Machine, p. 125 *Extensions*	2, 6, 7, 8 *3, 4, 5*	3.OA.4; 3.OA.5; 3.OA.6; 3.OA.7; 3.OA.8; 3.OA.9; 3.NBT.2; 3.NBT.3; 3.NF.1
Make Ten, p. 126 *Extensions*	2, 5, 6	3.NBT.2 *3.NBT.1*

Activity	Practices	Standards
Marble Probability, p. 127 *Extensions*	2, 4, 5, 6 *3, 7*	3.MD.3 *3.OA.3; 3.OA.4; 3.OA.7; 3.OA.8; 3.OA.9*
Mental Math Pushups, p. 128	1, 2, 6, 7	3.OA.4; 3.OA.5; 3.OA.7; 3.NBT.2
Message Relationships, p. 129	2, 3, 6	3.OA.4; 3.OA.5; 3.NBT.2; 3.NF.1; 3.MD.1
Multiplying Us, p. 131	1, 4, 5, 6, 8	3.OA.1; 3.OA.3; 3.OA.4; 3.OA.5; 3.OA.7
Pica Ferme Nada, p. 132	1, 2, 3, 6, 8	1.NBT.1
Piloting, p. 134	1, 2, 6	None
Ruler Around the Room, p. 135	2, 3, 5, 6	3.MD.4; 3.MD.8
Spinner Probability, p. 137 *Extension*	2, 3, 4, 5, 6	3.OA.3; 3.OA.4; 3.OA.5; 3.OA.7; 3.OA.9 *3.MD.3*
Tens, p. 139 *Variation 2*	2, 8	3.OA.9; 3.NBT.2 *3.NF.1; 3.NF.3c*
Things in Groups #1, p. 140 *Extension*	1, 2, 3, 6 *4, 5*	3.OA.1; 3.OA.3; 3.OA.4; 3.OA.5; 3.OA.7; 3.OA.8

Common Core Correlation by Mathematical **Practices**

Practice	Activities
1 Make sense of problems and persevere in solving them.	Base Ten Block Building, p. 109; Body Math, p. 111; Dimensions in the Bubble, p. 116; Double This, p. 118; Equations and Pictures, p. 119; Isosceles Triangle Message, p. 124; Mental Math Pushups, p. 128; Multiplying Us, p. 131; Pica Ferme Nada, p. 132; Piloting, p. 134; Things in Groups #1, p. 140
2 Reason abstractly and quantitatively.	Base Ten Block Building, p. 109; Beach Ball Tossing, p. 110; Body Math, p. 111; Clock Check-In, p. 112; Coin Flip Probability, p. 114; Digit Pop, p. 115; Dimensions in the Bubble, p. 116; Double This, p. 118; Equations and Pictures, p. 119; Examining Temperatures, p. 120; How Long Will It Bounce?, p. 122; How Much Money?, p. 123; Isosceles Triangle Message, p. 124; Magical Mystery Machine, p. 125; Make Ten, p. 126; Marble Probability, p. 127; Mental Math Pushups, p. 128; Message Relationships, p. 129; Pica Ferme Nada, p. 132; Piloting, p. 134; Ruler Around the Room, p. 135; Spinner Probability, p. 137; Tens, p. 139; Things in Groups #1, p. 140
3 Construct viable arguments and critique the reasoning of others.	Clock Check-In, p. 112; Coin Flip Probability, p. 114; Digit Pop, p. 115; Dimensions in the Bubble, p. 116; Equations and Pictures, p. 119; Examining Temperatures, p. 120; How Long Will It Bounce?, p. 122; How Much Money?, p. 123; Magical Mystery Machine (extensions), p. 125; Marble Probability (extensions), p. 127; Message Relationships, p. 129; Pica Ferme Nada, p. 132; Ruler Around the Room, p. 135; Spinner Probability, p. 137; Things in Groups #1, p. 140
4 Model with mathematics.	Base Ten Block Building, p. 109; Beach Ball Tossing, p. 110; Clock Check-In (extension), p. 112; Coin Flip Probability, p. 114; Equations and Pictures, p. 119; Examining Temperatures, p. 120; How Long Will It Bounce? (extension), p. 122; How Much Money?, p. 123; Magical Mystery Machine (extensions), p. 125; Marble Probability, p. 127; Multiplying Us, p. 131; Spinner Probability, p. 137; Things in Groups #1 (extension), p. 140
5 Use appropriate tools strategically.	Base Ten Block Building, p. 109; Dimensions in the Bubble, p. 116; How Long Will It Bounce?, p. 122; How Much Money?, p. 123; Isosceles Triangle Message, p. 124; Magical Mystery Machine (extensions), p. 125; Make Ten, p. 126; Marble Probability, p. 127; Multiplying Us, p. 131; Ruler Around the Room, p. 135; Spinner Probability, p. 137; Things in Groups #1 (extension), p. 140
6 Attend to precision.	Beach Ball Tossing, p. 110; Body Math, p. 111; Clock Check-In, p. 112; Coin Flip Probability, p. 114; Digit Pop, p. 115; Dimensions in the Bubble, p. 116; Double This, p. 118; Equations and Pictures, p. 119; How Much Money?, p. 123; Isosceles Triangle Message, p. 124; Magical Mystery Machine, p. 125; Make Ten, p. 126; Marble Probability, p. 127; Mental Math Pushups, p. 128; Message Relationships, p. 129; Multiplying Us, p. 131; Pica Ferme Nada, p. 132; Piloting, p. 134; Ruler Around the Room, p. 135; Spinner Probability, p. 137; Things in Groups #1, p. 140
7 Look for and make use of structure.	Base Ten Block Building, p. 109; Body Math, p. 111; Coin Flip Probability, p. 114; Digit Pop, p. 115; Examining Temperatures, p. 120; Isosceles Triangle Message, p. 124; Magical Mystery Machine, p. 125; Marble Probability (extensions), p. 127; Mental Math Pushups, p. 128
8 Look for and express regularity in repeated reasoning.	Double This, p. 118; Magical Mystery Machine, p. 125; Multiplying Us, p. 131; Pica Ferme Nada, p. 132; Tens, p. 139

Standards	Activities
3.OA.1 Interpret products of whole numbers	Base Ten Block Building (variation 2), p. 109; Beach Ball Tossing, p. 110; Double This, p. 118; Equations and Pictures, p. 119; How Much Money?, p. 123; Multiplying Us, p. 131; Things in Groups #1, p. 140
3.OA.2	None
3.OA.3 Use multiplication and division within 100 to solve word problems	Base Ten Block Building (variation 2), p. 109; Body Math, p. 111; Dimensions in the Bubble, p. 116; Double This, p. 118; Equations and Pictures, p. 119; How Much Money?, p. 123; Marble Probability (extensions), p. 127; Multiplying Us, p. 131; Spinner Probability, p. 137; Things in Groups #1, p. 140
3.OA.4 Determine the unknown whole number in a multiplication or division equation	Base Ten Block Building (variation 2), p. 109; Beach Ball Tossing, p. 110; Dimensions in the Bubble, p. 116; Double This, p. 118; Equations and Pictures, p. 119; How Much Money?, p. 123; Magical Mystery Machine, p. 125; Marble Probability (extensions), p. 127; Mental Math Pushups, p. 128; Message Relationships, p. 129; Multiplying Us, p. 131; Spinner Probability, p. 137; Things in Groups #1, p. 140
3.OA.5 Apply properties of operations as strategies to multiply and divide	Base Ten Block Building (variation 2), p. 109; Beach Ball Tossing, p. 110; Equations and Pictures, p. 119; How Much Money?, p. 123; Magical Mystery Machine, p. 125; Mental Math Pushups, p. 128; Message Relationships, p. 129; Multiplying Us, p. 131; Spinner Probability, p. 137; Things in Groups #1, p. 140
3.OA.6 Understand division as an unknown-factor problem	Body Math, p. 111; Magical Mystery Machine, p. 125
3.OA.7 Fluently multiply and divide within 100	Base Ten Block Building (variation 2), p. 109; Beach Ball Tossing, p. 110; Dimensions in the Bubble, p. 116; Double This, p. 118; Equations and Pictures, p. 119; How Much Money?, p. 123; Magical Mystery Machine, p. 125; Marble Probability (extensions), p. 127; Mental Math Pushups, p. 128; Multiplying Us, p. 131; Spinner Probability, p. 137; Things in Groups #1, p. 140
3.OA.8 Solve two-step word problems using the four operations	How Long Will It Bounce?, p. 122; How Much Money?, p. 123; Magical Mystery Machine, p. 125; Marble Probability (extensions), p. 127; Things in Groups #1, p. 140
3.OA.9 Identify arithmetic patterns . . . and explain them using properties of operations	Coin Flip Probability, p. 114; Digit Pop, p. 115; Double This, p. 118; Equations and Pictures, p. 119; Examining Temperatures, p. 120; How Much Money?, p. 123; Magical Mystery Machine, p. 125; Marble Probability (extensions), p. 127; Spinner Probability, p. 137; Tens, p. 139
3.NBT.1 Round whole numbers to the nearest 10 or 100	Base Ten Block Building, p. 109; Make Ten (extensions), p. 126; Pica Ferme Nada, p. 132
3.NBT.2 Fluently add and subtract within 1000	Base Ten Block Building, p. 109; Beach Ball Tossing, p. 110; Coin Flip Probability, p. 114; Digit Pop, p. 115; Examining Temperatures, p. 120; How Long Will It Bounce?, p. 122; How Much Money?, p. 123; Magical Mystery Machine, p. 125; Make Ten, p. 126; Mental Math Pushups, p. 128; Message Relationships, p. 129; Tens, p. 139

Standards	Activities
3.NBT.3 Multiply one-digit whole numbers by multiples of 10	Base Ten Block Building (variation 2), p. 109; Beach Ball Tossing, p. 110; How Much Money?, p. 123; Magical Mystery Machine, p. 125
3.NF.1 Understand a fraction 1/*b* as the quantity formed by 1 part when a whole is partitioned into *b* equal parts	Beach Ball Tossing (variations), p. 110; Body Math, p. 111; Dimensions in the Bubble, p. 116; Equations and Pictures (variation), p. 119; How Much Money?, p. 123; Magical Mystery Machine, p. 125; Message Relationships, p. 129; Tens (variation 2), p. 139
3.NF.2a–b	None
3.NF.3a–d Explain equivalence of fractions	Beach Ball Tossing (variations), p. 110; Body Math, p. 111; Equations and Pictures (variation), p. 119; Tens (variation 2), p. 139 (c only)
3.MD.1 Tell and write time to the nearest minute	Clock Check-In, p. 112; How Long Will It Bounce?, p. 122; Message Relationships, p. 129
3.MD.2	None
3.MD.3 Draw a scaled picture graph and a scaled bar graph to represent a data set	Clock Check-In (extension), p. 112; Coin Flip Probability, p. 114; Examining Temperatures, p. 120; How Long Will It Bounce? (extension), p. 122; Marble Probability, p. 127; Spinner Probability (extension), p. 137
3.MD.4 Generate measurement data	Dimensions in the Bubble, p. 116; Ruler Around the Room, p. 135
3.MD.5a–b Recognize area	Dimensions in the Bubble, p. 116
3.MD.6 Measure areas by counting unit squares	Dimensions in the Bubble, p. 116
3.MD.7a–d Relate area to the operations of multiplication and addition	Dimensions in the Bubble, p. 116
3.MD.8 Solve . . . problems involving perimeters of polygons	Dimensions in the Bubble, p. 116; Ruler Around the Room, p. 135
3.G.1 Understand that shapes . . . may share attributes	Isosceles Triangle Message, p. 124
3.G.2 Partition shapes into parts with equal areas	Isosceles Triangle Message, p. 124

Activity	Practices	Standards
Algebra Card Game, p. 143 *Variation*	1, 2, 4, 5, 6	4.OA.1; 4.OA.4; 4.NBT.2; 4.NBT.4 *4.NF.3a–c; 4.NF.6; 4.MD.1*
Attribution Messages, p. 144	3, 4, 6, 7	4.MD.5; 4.G.1; 4.G.2; 4.G.3
Bacon and Eggs, p. 146	2, 6, 7, 8	4.OA.4; 4.OA.5
Bar Graphing Favorites, p. 147 *Extension*	4, 6 *2, 3*	*4.OA.3*
Battery Algebra, p. 149	1, 2, 3, 4, 8	4.OA.2; 4.OA.3; 4.OA.5; 4.NBT.4; 4.NF.3a, c, d; 4.NF.4a, c; 4.NF.6
Coded Messages, p. 150	1, 2, 4, 5, 6	None
Coin Combinations, p. 151	1, 3, 4, 7, 8	4.OA.3; 4.NBT.4; 4.NBT.5; 4.MD.2
Estimate the Amount, p. 152	1, 2, 5	4.OA.3; 4.NBT.5
Estimating and Measuring, p. 153	1, 2, 4, 5, 6	4.MD.1; 4.MD.3
Fencing In an Area, p. 155	1, 3, 4, 5, 7	4.OA.3; 4.OA.5; 4.NBT.4; 4.NBT.5; 4.MD.1; 4.MD.2; 4.MD.3
How Do We Relate?, p. 157	1, 2, 3, 4, 6	4.OA.1; 4.OA.4; 4.NBT.1; 4.NBT.2; 4.NBT.4; 4.NF.1; 4.NF.2
How Many Ways, p. 158	1, 2, 3, 4, 6	4.OA.3; 4.NBT.4; 4.NBT.5; 4.NF.3a, d
How Tall Would We Be?, p. 159 *Extensions*	1, 2, 3, 5, 8 *4, 6*	4.OA.3; 4.NBT.3; 4.NBT.4; 4.MD.1; 4.MD.2
Make a Line Segment Animal, p. 160	1, 3, 5, 7, 8	4.MD.1; 4.G.1
Make a Polygon Animal, p. 161	1, 2, 3, 5, 7	4.G.2
Making Change for a Dollar, p. 163	1, 2, 3, 4, 6	4.NBT.2; 4.NBT.4; 4.NBT.5; 4.MD.2
Match Card Greeting, p. 164 *Variations/Extensions*	1, 2, 4, 6, 7	4.NBT.2; 4.NBT.4 *4.OA.2; 4.OA.3; 4.NF.3d;* *4.NF.4c; 4.MD.2*

Activity	Practices	Standards
Newspaper Connections, p. 165	2, 3, 4, 6	Varies, depending on number connection(s)
Pass the Deck Operations, p. 166 *Variations*	1, 2, 6 *7*	4.NBT.4; 4.NBT.5; 4.NBT.6 *4.NF.3a, c; 4.G.2*
Pattern Chanting, p. 167 *Extension*	1, 2, 3, 6, 7	4.OA.5; 4.NBT.1; 4.NBT.4; 4.G.1; 4.G.2 *4.NF.3a; 4.NF.5*
Sharing Milk, p. 168	1, 3, 4, 5, 8	4.OA.2; 4.OA.5; 4.NF.3d; 4.NF.4c; 4.MD.1; 4.MD.2
Spider Web, p. 170 *Extensions*	2, 3, 7 *1, 4, 5, 6*	4.MD.3; 4.G.1; 4.G.2; 4.G.3
Split the Group, p. 171	1, 2, 4, 5, 6	4.OA.2; 4.OA.3; 4.NBT.2; 4.NBT.6
Split Up the Bags, p. 172	1, 3, 4, 5, 6	4.OA.2; 4.OA.3; 4.NBT.2; 4.NBT.6
Things in Groups #2, p. 173	1, 2, 4, 6, 7	4.OA.2; 4.OA.3; 4.NBT.2; 4.NBT.4; 4.NBT.5

Practice	Activities
1 Make sense of problems and persevere in solving them.	Algebra Card Game, p. 143; Battery Algebra, p. 149; Coded Messages, p. 150; Coin Combinations, p. 151; Estimate the Amount, p. 152; Estimating and Measuring, p. 153; Fencing In an Area, p. 155; How Do We Relate?, p. 157; How Many Ways, p. 158; How Tall Would We Be?, p. 159; Make a Line Segment Animal, p. 160; Make a Polygon Animal, p. 161; Making Change for a Dollar, p. 163; Match Card Greeting, p. 164; Pass the Deck Operations, p. 166; Pattern Chanting, p. 167; Sharing Milk, p. 168; Spider Web (extensions), p. 170; Split the Group, p. 171; Split Up the Bags, p. 172; Things in Groups #2, p. 173
2 Reason abstractly and quantitatively.	Algebra Card Game, p. 143; Bacon and Eggs, p. 146; Bar Graphing Favorites (extension), p. 147; Battery Algebra, p. 149; Coded Messages, p. 150; Estimate the Amount, p. 152; Estimating and Measuring, p. 153; How Do We Relate?, p. 157; How Many Ways, p. 158; How Tall Would We Be?, p. 159; Make a Polygon Animal, p. 161; Making Change for a Dollar, p. 163; Match Card Greeting, p. 164; Newspaper Connections, p. 165; Pass the Deck Operations, p. 166; Pattern Chanting, p. 167; Spider Web, p. 170; Split the Group, p. 171; Things in Groups #2, p. 173
3 Construct viable arguments and critique the reasoning of others.	Attribution Messages, p. 144; Bar Graphing Favorites (extension), p. 147; Battery Algebra, p. 149; Coin Combinations, p. 151; Fencing In an Area, p. 155; How Do We Relate?, p. 157; How Many Ways, p. 158; How Tall Would We Be?, p. 159; Make a Line Segment Animal, p. 160; Make a Polygon Animal, p. 161; Making Change for a Dollar, p. 163; Newspaper Connections, p. 165; Pattern Chanting, p. 167; Sharing Milk, p. 168; Spider Web, p. 170; Split Up the Bags, p. 172
4 Model with mathematics.	Algebra Card Game, p. 143; Attribution Messages, p. 144; Bar Graphing Favorites, p. 147; Battery Algebra, p. 149; Coded Messages, p. 150; Coin Combinations, p. 151; Estimating and Measuring, p. 153; Fencing In an Area, p. 155; How Do We Relate?, p. 157; How Many Ways, p. 158; How Tall Would We Be? (extensions), p. 159; Making Change for a Dollar, p. 163; Match Card Greeting, p. 164; Newspaper Connections, p. 165; Sharing Milk, p. 168; Spider Web (extensions), p. 170; Split the Group, p. 171; Split Up the Bags, p. 172; Things in Groups #2, p. 173
5 Use appropriate tools strategically.	Algebra Card Game, p. 143; Coded Messages, p. 150; Estimate the Amount, p. 152; Estimating and Measuring, p. 153; Fencing In an Area, p. 155; How Tall Would We Be?, p. 159; Make a Line Segment Animal, p. 160; Make a Polygon Animal, p. 161; Sharing Milk, p. 168; Spider Web (extensions), p. 170; Split the Group, p. 171; Split Up the Bags, p. 172
6 Attend to precision.	Algebra Card Game, p. 143; Attribution Messages, p. 144; Bacon and Eggs, p. 146; Bar Graphing Favorites, p. 147; Coded Messages, p. 150; Estimating and Measuring, p. 153; How Do We Relate?, p. 157; How Many Ways, p. 158; How Tall Would We Be? (extensions), p. 159; Making Change for a Dollar, p. 163; Match Card Greeting, p. 164; Newspaper Connections, p. 165; Pass the Deck Operations, p. 166; Pattern Chanting, p. 167; Spider Web (extensions), p. 170; Split the Group, p. 171; Split Up the Bags, p. 172; Things in Groups #2, p. 173
7 Look for and make use of structure.	Attribution Messages, p. 144; Bacon and Eggs, p. 146; Coin Combinations, p. 151; Fencing In an Area, p. 155; Make a Line Segment Animal, p. 160; Make a Polygon Animal, p. 161; Match Card Greeting, p. 164; Pass the Deck Operations (variations), p. 166; Pattern Chanting, p. 167; Spider Web, p. 170; Things in Groups #2, p. 173
8 Look for and express regularity in repeated reasoning.	Bacon and Eggs, p. 146; Battery Algebra, p. 149; Coin Combinations, p. 151; How Tall Would We Be?, p. 159; Make a Line Segment Animal, p. 160; Sharing Milk, p. 168

Grade Level

4 Common Core Correlation by Mathematical **Standards**

Standards	Activities
4.OA.1 Interpret a multiplication equation as a comparison	Algebra Card Game, p. 143; How Do We Relate?, p. 157
4.OA.2 Multiply or divide to solve word problems	Battery Algebra, p. 149; Match Card Greeting (variations/extensions), p. 164; Sharing Milk, p. 168; Split the Group, p. 171; Split Up the Bags, p. 172; Things in Groups #2, p. 173
4.OA.3 Solve multistep word problems . . . using the four operations	Bar Graphing Favorites (extension), p. 147; Battery Algebra, p. 149; Coin Combinations, p. 151; Estimate the Amount, p. 152; Fencing In an Area, p. 155; How Many Ways, p. 158; How Tall Would We Be?, p. 159; Match Card Greeting (variations/extensions), p. 164; Split the Group, p. 171; Split Up the Bags, p. 172; Things in Groups #2, p. 173
4.OA.4 Find all factor pairs for a whole number in the range 1–100	Algebra Card Game, p. 143; Bacon and Eggs, p. 146; How Do We Relate?, p. 157
4.OA.5 Generate a number or shape pattern that follows a given rule	Bacon and Eggs, p. 146; Battery Algebra, p. 149; Fencing In an Area, p. 155; Pattern Chanting, p. 167; Sharing Milk, p. 168
4.NBT.1 Recognize that . . . a digit in one place represents ten times what it represents in the place to its right	How Do We Relate?, p. 157; Pattern Chanting, p. 167
4.NBT.2 Read and write multi-digit whole numbers	Algebra Card Game, p. 143; How Do We Relate?, p. 157; Making Change for a Dollar, p. 163; Match Card Greeting, p. 164; Split the Group, p. 171; Split Up the Bags, p. 172; Things in Groups #2, p. 173
4.NBT.3 Use place value understanding to round multi-digit whole numbers	How Tall Would We Be?, p. 159
4.NBT.4 Fluently add and subtract multi-digit whole numbers using the standard algorithm	Algebra Card Game, p. 143; Battery Algebra, p. 149; Coin Combinations, p. 151; Fencing In an Area, p. 155; How Do We Relate?, p. 157; How Many Ways, p. 158; How Tall Would We Be?, p. 159; Making Change for a Dollar, p. 163; Match Card Greeting, p. 164; Pass the Deck Operations, p. 166; Pattern Chanting, p. 167; Things in Groups #2, p. 173
4.NBT.5 Multiply a whole number of up to four digits	Coin Combinations, p. 151; Estimate the Amount, p. 152; Fencing In an Area, p. 155; How Many Ways, p. 158; Making Change for a Dollar, p. 163; Pass the Deck Operations, p. 166; Things in Groups #2, p. 173
4.NBT.6 Find whole-number quotients and remainders	Pass the Deck Operations, p. 166; Split the Group, p. 171; Split Up the Bags, p. 172
4.NF.1 Explain why a fraction a/b is equivalent to a fraction $(n \times a)/(n \times b)$	How Do We Relate?, p. 157

245

Standards	Activities
4.NF.2 Compare two fractions	How Do We Relate?, p. 157
4.NF.3	None
4.NF.3a–d Understand addition and subtraction of fractions; decompose a fraction; add and subtract mixed numbers; solve word problems . . . of fractions	Algebra Card Game (variation), p. 143 (a–c only); Battery Algebra, p. 149 (a, c, d only); How Many Ways, p. 158 (a, d only); Match Card Greeting (variations/extensions), p. 164 (d only); Pass the Deck Operations (variations), p. 166 (a,c only); Pattern Chanting (extension), p. 167 (a only); Sharing Milk, p. 168 (d only)
4.NF.4	None
4.NF.4a–c Understand a fraction a/b as a multiple of $1/b$; understand a multiple of a/b as a multiple of $1/b$; solve word problems involving multiplication of a fraction	Battery Algebra, p. 149 (a, c only); Match Card Greeting (variations/extensions), p. 164 (c only); Sharing Milk, p. 168 (c only)
4.NF.5 Express a fraction with denominator 10 as an equivalent fraction with denominator 100	Pattern Chanting (extension), p. 167
4.NF.6 Use decimal notation for fractions with denominators 10 or 100	Algebra Card Game (variation), p. 143; Battery Algebra, p. 149
4.NF.7	None
4.MD.1 Know relative sizes of measurement units within one system of units	Algebra Card Game (variation), p. 143; Estimating and Measuring, p. 153; Fencing In an Area, p. 155; How Tall Would We Be?, p. 159; Make a Line Segment Animal, p. 160; Sharing Milk, p. 168
4.MD.2 Use the four operations to solve word problems involving distances, intervals of time, liquid volumes, masses of objects, and money	Coin Combinations, p. 151; Fencing In an Area, p. 155; How Tall Would We Be?, p. 159; Making Change for a Dollar, p. 163; Match Card Greeting (variations/extensions), p. 164; Sharing Milk, p. 168
4.MD.3 Apply the area and perimeter formulas for rectangles	Estimating and Measuring, p. 153; Fencing In an Area, p. 155; Spider Web, p. 170
4.MD.4	None
4.MD.5 Recognize angles as geometric shapes	Attribution Messages, p. 144

Standards	Activities
4.MD.5a–b	None
4.MD.6	None
4.MD.7	None
4.G.1 Draw points, lines, segments, rays, angles . . . and perpendicular and parallel lines	Attribution Messages, p. 144; Make a Line Segment Animal, p. 160; Pattern Chanting, p. 167; Spider Web, p. 170
4.G.2 Classify two-dimensional figures	Attribution Messages, p. 144; Make a Polygon Animal, p. 161; Pass the Deck Operations (variations), p. 166; Pattern Chanting, p. 167; Spider Web, p. 170
4.G.3 Recognize a line of symmetry	Attribution Messages, p. 144; Spider Web, p. 170

Grade Level

5   Common Core Math Correlation by **Activities**

Activity	Practices	Standards
Average Age, p. 175 *Extension*	1 2, 3, 6 *4*	5.NBT.6 *5.G.1; 5.G.2*
Batting Averages Message, p. 177	1, 2, 4, 5, 6	5.OA.2; 5.NBT.6; 5.NF.1; 5.NF.2; 5.NF.3
Beach Raft Message, p. 178	2, 3, 4, 7, 8	5.NBT.6; 5.NF.4b; 5.NF.6; 5.NF.7c
Continuous Sum Fractions, p. 179 *Extension*	1, 2, 6, 8	5.NF.1 *5.NBT.7*
Crane Problem, p. 180 *Variation*	1, 2, 3, 4, 6	5.NF.5a *5.MD.1*
Describe the Item, p. 181	2, 6, 7	5.G.3; 5.G.4
Figure Making, p. 182	1, 2, 3, 5, 7	5.G.3; 5.G.4
Finding Area and Perimeter, p. 183	1, 3, 4, 5, 7	5.OA.2; 5.NBT.5; 5.NF.1; 5.NF.4a–b; 5.NF.6; 5.G.4
Flip Card Game, p. 185	1, 2, 3, 6, 8	5.NBT.1; 5.NBT.4; 5.NBT.7; 5.NF.1; 5.NF.4a; 5.NF.5a–b
Grab and Attribute, p. 186	2, 3, 6, 7	5.MD.3; 5.MD.4; 5.MD.5
Group Memory, p. 187	1, 2, 6	5.NBT.5; 5.NBT.6; 5.NBT.7; 5.NF.1; 5.NF.4; 5.NF.7
Matching and Drawing, p. 188	1, 2, 3, 4, 6	5.NBT.3a–b; 5.NBT.7; 5.NF.3
Mixed Number Making, p. 189 *Extension 2*	1, 2, 3, 4, 6	*5.NF.1; 5.NF.2*
Name Values Multiplication, p. 191	1, 2, 3, 4, 6	5.OA.2
Our Metric Heights, p. 192	2, 3, 4, 5, 6	5.NBT.3a–b; 5.NBT.4; 5.NBT.7; 5.MD.1
Scaling Floor Layouts, p. 193 *Extension 2*	1, 4, 5, 6, 7	5.MD.1 *5.NBT.5*
Shooting Percentages, p. 195	1, 2, 4, 5, 6	5.OA.2; 5.NBT.6; 5.NF.1; 5.NF.2; 5.NF.3

Activity	Practices	Standards
Snowman Message, p. 196	1, 3, 4, 5, 8	5.MD.1; 5.MD.3; 5.MD.5
Toss and Call with Numbers, p. 197	2, 3, 6, 7, 8	Varies, depending on operation(s) used
Toss and Call with Operations, p. 198	1, 2, 6, 8	Varies, depending on operation(s) used
The Wall Message, p. 199	1, 3, 4, 5, 7	5.OA.1; 5.OA.2; 5.NBT.1; 5.NBT.5; 5.NF.5a; 5.MD.1; 5.MD.3; 5.MD.4; 5.MD.5
What Would Cover It?, p. 200	1, 2, 3, 4, 7	5.OA.2; 5.NBT.7; 5.NF.1; 5.NF.4a–b; 5.NF.6; 5.MD.1; 5.MD.3; 5.MD.4; 5.MD.5
What's Our Sum Decimals, p. 202	1, 2, 6	5.NBT.1; 5.NBT.3a–b; 5.NBT.7
What's Our Sum Fractions, p. 203	1, 2, 6	5.NF.1; 5.NF.2
Which One Doesn't Belong?, p. 204	2, 3	5.OA.3; 5.NBT.1

Practice	Activities
1 Make sense of problems and persevere in solving them.	Average Age, p. 175; Batting Averages Message, p. 177; Continuous Sum Fractions, p. 179; Crane Problem, p. 180; Figure Making, p. 182; Finding Area and Perimeter, p. 183; Flip Card Game, p. 185; Group Memory, p. 187; Matching and Drawing, p. 188; Mixed Number Making, p. 189; Name Values Multiplication, p. 191; Scaling Floor Layouts, p. 193; Shooting Percentages, p. 195; Snowman Message, p. 196; Toss and Call with Operations, p. 198; The Wall Message, p. 199; What Would Cover It?, p. 200; What's Our Sum Decimals, p. 202; What's Our Sum Fractions, p. 203
2 Reason abstractly and quantitatively.	Average Age, p. 175; Batting Averages Message, p. 177; Beach Raft Message, p. 178; Continuous Sum Fractions, p. 179; Crane Problem, p. 180; Describe the Item, p. 181; Figure Making, p. 182; Flip Card Game, p. 185; Grab and Attribute, p. 186; Group Memory, p. 187; Matching and Drawing, p. 188; Mixed Number Making, p. 189; Name Values Multiplication, p. 191; Our Metric Heights, p. 192; Shooting Percentages, p. 195; Toss and Call with Numbers, p. 197; Toss and Call with Operations, p. 198; What Would Cover It?, p. 200; What's Our Sum Decimals, p. 202; What's Our Sum Fractions, p. 203; Which One Doesn't Belong?, p. 204
3 Construct viable arguments and critique the reasoning of others.	Average Age, p. 175; Beach Raft Message, p. 178; Crane Problem, p. 180; Figure Making, p. 182; Finding Area and Perimeter, p. 183; Flip Card Game, p. 185; Grab and Attribute, p. 186; Matching and Drawing, p. 188; Mixed Number Making, p. 189; Name Values Multiplication, p. 191; Our Metric Heights, p. 192; Snowman Message, p. 196; Toss and Call with Numbers, p. 197; The Wall Message, p. 199; What Would Cover It?, p. 200; Which One Doesn't Belong?, p. 204
4 Model with mathematics.	Average Age (extension), p. 175; Batting Averages Message, p. 177; Beach Raft Message, p. 178; Crane Problem, p. 180; Finding Area and Perimeter, p. 183; Matching and Drawing, p. 188; Mixed Number Making, p. 189; Name Values Multiplication, p. 191; Our Metric Heights, p. 192; Scaling Floor Layouts, p. 193; Shooting Percentages, p. 195; Snowman Message, p. 196; The Wall Message, p. 199; What Would Cover It?, p. 200
5 Use appropriate tools strategically.	Batting Averages Message, p. 177; Figure Making, p. 182; Finding Area and Perimeter, p. 183; Our Metric Heights, p. 192; Scaling Floor Layouts, p. 193; Shooting Percentages, p. 195; Snowman Message, p. 196; The Wall Message, p. 199
6 Attend to precision.	Average Age, p. 175; Batting Averages Message, p. 177; Continuous Sum Fractions, p. 179; Crane Problem, p. 180; Describe the Item, p. 181; Flip Card Game, p. 185; Grab and Attribute, p. 186; Group Memory, p. 187; Matching and Drawing, p. 188; Mixed Number Making, p. 189; Name Values Multiplication, p. 191; Our Metric Heights, p. 192; Scaling Floor Layouts, p. 193; Shooting Percentages, p. 195; Toss and Call with Numbers, p. 197; Toss and Call with Operations, p. 198; What's Our Sum Decimals, p. 202; What's Our Sum Fractions, p. 203
7 Look for and make use of structure.	Beach Raft Message, p. 178; Describe the Item, p. 181; Figure Making, p. 182; Finding Area and Perimeter, p. 183; Grab and Attribute, p. 186; Scaling Floor Layouts, p. 193; Toss and Call with Numbers, p. 197; The Wall Message, p. 199; What Would Cover It?, p. 200
8 Look for and express regularity in repeated reasoning.	Beach Raft Message, p. 178; Continuous Sum Fractions, p. 179; Flip Card Game, p. 185; Snowman Message, p. 196; Toss and Call with Numbers, p. 197; Toss and Call with Operations, p. 198

Common Core Correlation by Mathematical **Standards**

Standards	Activities
5.OA.1 Use parentheses, brackets, or braces in numerical expressions	The Wall Message, p. 199
5.OA.2 Write simple expressions that record calculations with numbers	Batting Averages Message, p. 177; Finding Area and Perimeter, p. 183; Name Values Multiplication, p. 191; Shooting Percentages, p. 195; The Wall Message, p. 199; What Would Cover It?, p. 200
5.OA.3 Generate two numerical patterns using two given rules	Which One Doesn't Belong?, p. 204
5.NBT.1 Recognize that . . . a digit in one place represents 10 times as much as it represents in the place to its right and 1/10 of what it represents in the place to its left	Flip Card Game, p. 185; The Wall Message, p. 199; What's Our Sum Decimals, p. 202; Which One Doesn't Belong?, p. 204
5.NBT.2	None
5.NBT.3	None
5.NBT.3a–b Read and write decimals to thousandths; compare two decimals to thousandths	Matching and Drawing, p. 188; Our Metric Heights, p. 192; What's Our Sum Decimals, p. 202
5.NBT.4 Round decimals to any place	Flip Card Game, p. 185; Our Metric Heights, p. 192
5.NBT.5 Fluently multiply multi-digit whole numbers	Finding Area and Perimeter, p. 183; Group Memory, p. 187; Scaling Floor Layouts (extension 2), p. 193; The Wall Message, p. 199
5.NBT.6 Find whole-number quotients	Average Age, p. 175; Batting Averages Message, p. 177; Beach Raft Message, p. 178; Group Memory, p. 187; Shooting Percentages, p. 195
5.NBT.7 Add, subtract, multiply, and divide decimals to hundredths	Continuous Sum Fractions (extension), p. 179; Flip Card Game, p. 185; Group Memory, p. 187; Matching and Drawing, p. 188; Our Metric Heights, p. 192; What Would Cover It?, p. 200; What's Our Sum Decimals, p. 202
5.NF.1 Add and subtract fractions with unlike denominators	Batting Averages Message, p. 177; Continuous Sum Fractions, p. 179; Finding Area and Perimeter, p. 183; Flip Card Game, p. 185; Group Memory, p. 187; Mixed Number Making (extension 2), p. 189; Shooting Percentages, p. 195; What Would Cover It?, p. 200; What's Our Sum Fractions, p. 203
5.NF.2 Solve word problems involving addition and subtraction of fractions	Batting Averages Message, p. 177; Mixed Number Making (extension 2), p. 189; Shooting Percentages, p. 195; What's Our Sum Fractions, p. 203

Standards	Activities
5.NF.3 Interpret a fraction as division of the numerator by the denominator	Batting Averages Message, p. 177; Matching and Drawing, p. 188; Shooting Percentages, p. 195
5.NF.4 Apply and extend previous understandings of multiplication to multiply a fraction	Group Memory, p. 187
5.NF.4a–b Interpret the product (a/b) x q as a parts of a partition of q into b equal parts; find the area of a rectangle with fractional side lengths	Beach Raft Message, p. 178 (b only); Finding Area and Perimeter, p. 183; Flip Card Game, p. 185 (a only); What Would Cover It?, p. 200
5.NF.5	None
5.NF.5a–b Comparing the size of a product to the size of one factor; explaining why multiplying a given number by a fraction greater than 1 results in a product greater than the given number	Crane Problem, p. 180 (a only); Flip Card Game, p. 185; The Wall Message, p. 199 (a only)
5.NF.6 Solve real world problems involving multiplication of fractions and mixed numbers	Beach Raft Message, p. 178; Finding Area and Perimeter, p. 183; What Would Cover It?, p. 200
5.NF.7 Apply and extend understandings of division to divide unit fractions	Group Memory, p. 187
5.NF.7a–c Interpret division of a unit fraction by a non-zero whole number; interpret division of a whole number by a unit fraction; solve real world problems involving division of unit fractions	Beach Raft Message, p. 178 (c only)
5.MD.1 Convert among different-sized standard measurement units	Crane Problem, p. 180; Our Metric Heights, p. 192; Scaling Floor Layouts, p. 193; Snowman Message, p. 196; The Wall Message, p. 199; What Would Cover It?, p. 200
5.MD.2	None
5.MD.3 Recognize volume as an attribute of solid figures	Grab and Attribute, p. 186; Snowman Message, p. 196; The Wall Message, p. 199; What Would Cover It?, p. 200
5.MD.3a–b	None
5.MD.4 Measure volumes by counting unit cubes	Grab and Attribute, p. 186; The Wall Message, p. 199; What Would Cover It?, p. 200

5   Common Core Correlation by Mathematical **Standards**, cont.

Standards	Activities
5.MD.5 Relate volume to the operations of multiplication and addition	Grab and Attribute, p. 186; Snowman Message, p. 196; The Wall Message, p. 199; What Would Cover It?, p. 200
5.MD.5a–c	None
5.G.1 Use a pair of perpendicular number lines . . . to define a coordinate system	Average Age (extension), p. 175
5.G.2 Represent real world and mathematical problems by graphing points	Average Age (extension), p. 175
5.G.3 Understand that attributes belonging to a category of two-dimensional figures also belong to all subcategories of that category	Describe the Item, p. 181; Figure Making, p. 182
5.G.4 Classify two-dimensional figures	Describe the Item, p. 181; Figure Making, p. 182; Finding Area and Perimeter, p. 183

Related Resources

from Northeast Foundation for Children,
developer of the *Responsive Classroom®* approach:

The Morning Meeting Book
by Roxann Kriete, 2002

Doing Science in Morning Meeting
by Lara Webb and Margaret Berry Wilson, June 2013

80 Morning Meeting Ideas for Grades K–2
by Susan Lattanzi Roser, 2012

80 Morning Meeting Ideas for Grades 3–6
by Carol Davis, 2012

**99 Activities and Greetings: Great for Morning Meeting …
and other meetings, too!**
by Melissa Correa-Connolly, 2004

Morning Meeting Messages, K–6
by Rosalea S. Fisher, Eric Henry, and Deborah Porter,
with an introduction by Marlynn Clayton, 2006

Morning Meeting Professional Development Kit
Facilitator's guide, DVDs, resource books, 2008

**Energizers! 88 Quick Movement Activities
That Refresh and Refocus, K–6**
by Susan Lattanzi Roser, 2009

**Closing Circles: 50 Activities
for Ending the Day in a Positive Way**
by Dana Januszka and Kristen Vincent, 2012

For more information, visit www.responsiveclassroom.org

Andy Dousis taught third and fourth grades at Flanders School in East Lyme, Connecticut, for ten years. He then joined Northeast Foundation for Children (NEFC), coaching teachers and supporting schools impementing the *Responsive Classroom* approach to teaching. Andy is a state champion high school football coach and former Marine. He lives in East Lyme with his wife, Debbie, and their daughters, Shawn and Hunter.

Before coming to work at NEFC full-time, Margaret Berry Wilson worked as a classroom teacher in Nashville, Tennessee, for thirteen years and then in San Bernardino, California, for two years. She has been using the *Responsive Classroom* approach since 1998 and presenting *Responsive Classroom* workshops since 2004. She lives in Riverside, California, with her husband, Andy, their adorable son, Matthew, and new lovable dog, Fuzzy.

Northeast Foundation for Children, Inc., a not-for-profit educational organization, is the developer of the *Responsive Classroom*® approach to teaching. We offer the following for elementary school educators:

Publications and Resources

- Books, DVDs, and CDs for teachers and school leaders
- Professional development kits for school-based study
- Website with extensive library of free articles: www.responsiveclassroom.org
- Free quarterly newsletter for elementary educators
- The *Responsive*® blog, with news, ideas, and advice from and for elementary educators

Professional Development Services

- Introductory one-day workshops for teachers and administrators
- Week-long institutes offered nationwide each summer and on-site at schools
- Follow-up workshops and on-site consulting services to support implementation
- Resources for site-based study
- National conference for administrators and teacher leaders

Northeast Foundation for Children, Inc.
85 Avenue A, Suite 204, P.O. Box 718
Turners Falls, MA 01376-0718

800-360-6332   www.responsiveclassroom.org
info@responsiveclassroom.org